L'ISTOYRE DE JEHAN COQUAULT

A LITERARY FORGERY

L'ISTOYRE DE JEHAN COQUAULT

A LITERARY FORGERY

Edited by

Norris J. Lacy

French Literature Publications Company
York, South Carolina
1982

(Mod. Lang.)
(Circ. Chg.)

For S.A.M.

ACKNOWLEDGMENTS

During the preparation of this volume, I consulted a number of persons about particular segments of the text or about specific problems. I am happy to acknowledge the advice and assistance of the following: Moshé Lazar of the University of Southern California, Consuelo Wager Dutschke of the Huntington Library, Marilyn Stokstad and Barbara Craig of the University of Kansas, and Jerry Nash of the University of New Orleans. I hasten to note that this acknowledgment indicates my debt to them without implying that they necessarily share my views or conclusions. I am also grateful to my colleague John Williams, who first called the manuscript to my attention; to Alexandra Mason, Ann Hyde, and the staff of the Kenneth Spencer Research Library; to the University of Kansas for sabbatical leave and a research grant to facilitate my work on the *Istoyre de Jehan Coquault.*

CONTENTS

INTRODUCTION

The nineteenth-century fascination with things medieval is too well recognized to require demonstration here. That fascination frequently led people of means to acquire early artifacts, and if the real article was not available, a "modern medieval" item generally could be had (whether or not its modernity was recognized by the owner). This resurgence of medievalism was strong enough in some instances to create successful careers for purveyors of medievalia, real or counterfeit. The best-known example of such careers is doubtless that of the "Spanish Forger," who worked in or near Paris at the very end of the nineteenth century and the beginning of the twentieth, and who was skillful enough that many of his manuscripts and panels were until recently considered authentic works of the late Middle Ages or Renaissance.[1]

The manuscript presented in this volume was also prepared during the nineteenth century, although by someone considerably less skilled than the Spanish Forger. For no other reason than that it is a counterfeit, it merits at least passing notice. However, were it simply one more "fake" manuscript, like many others that repose in various libraries, it would not likely hold our attention for long. But the *Istoyre de Jehan Coquault* is of particular interest for several reasons. It is first of all notable that there is no apparent attempt on the part of the forger to defraud (by abrading and artificially "aging" the vellum, or by cracking the paint of the miniatures, for example). The nineteenth-century craftsman to whom we owe the manuscript may therefore have been content to have it recognized as modern.[2] Secondly, the manuscript goes a large step beyond most nineteenth-century imitations of medieval texts, in that this one purports to be a *translation* of a medieval text—but the language into which it is translated is of the *sixteenth century*. We are thus dealing with what we might call a "Victorian Renaissance medieval manuscript," a nineteenth-century manuscript which ostensibly offers a sixteenth-century rendering of an earlier text. Consequently, the questions of origin and transmission are particularly intriguing. Unfortunately, certain of those problems can be resolved only tentatively or not at all. The excellence of the language indicates that the work closely follows an antecedent text, but if so, that text is now apparently lost. Moreover, we have no information about the author or scribe, nor, indeed, do we even have knowledge of the manuscript's history prior to its 1963 entry in the catalogue of the University of Kansas.

One final reason (and perhaps the most persuasive one) for studying and editing the manuscript is, quite simply, that it offers us a very good story, a carefully crafted narrative that easily captures and keeps the reader's attention.

Thus, even though we know rather less than we would like to know about the manuscript and the work it preserves, it is an attractive example of nineteenth-century medievalism,[3] a fascinating historical and linguistic enigma, and a literary creation of some merit. It deserves to be known, and perhaps its publication will eventually enable us to provide some of the facts and answers we now lack.

I. THE MANUSCRIPT

A. Description

L'*Istoyre de Jehan Coquault* is preserved in MS A32 of the Kenneth Spencer Research Library of the University of Kansas. The text identifies itself as *Antiennes cronicques ne moing curieulzes que plaisantes* (fol. 1r), but by its form and content it is actually a short romance.[4] The manuscript is a small volume, measuring 142 x 95 mm. It contains fifty-eight unnumbered folios, of which the first one and last two are blank;[5] the text is on vellum, with a single column of approximately twenty-two lines per side. The writing, a conflation of a gothic book hand and a later humanistic script,[6] is neat and (with few exceptions) unusually legible. The binding is polished brown morocco and dates from the present century; it has a hubbed spine with the words "Anciennes Cronicques de Reims," followed by "Jean Coquault," giving the erroneous impression that Coquault is the author, rather than the character. The manuscript is of uncertain provenance, although a note inside the front board indicates that it was once part of the Walter B. Slater Collection. The circumstances of its acquisition by the University of Kansas were, unfortunately, not recorded.

The volume includes twenty-three illuminated initials, six to eight lines high; four of them are historiated. There is also a full-page miniature on fol. 1r, and numerous small red or blue initials adorn the text throughout. The copyist also uses various small red, blue, or gold leaf ornaments to fill out any line of text that does not extend to the right margin.

B. The Miniatures

1. Full-page miniature (fol. 1r) of a seated man writing a manuscript. The figure is dressed in a rather shapeless robe, and while the face is adequately drawn, the writing hand has long, sausage-like fingers. The floor of the room is tiled, with the tiles exhibiting realistic perspective from front to back. On the other hand, the copy stand and the canopied top of the copyist's chair are seriously distorted in their perspective. The impression is that a figure and furniture, taken perhaps from some other source, were placed into a more realistically depicted room.

The paint is applied heavily with short, indelicate strokes; the colors are for the most part dull tones of brown, gray, and olive.

A simple foliate design adorns the top, bottom, and left side of the miniature. The scene includes a square unpainted section, within which are the words "Antiennes cronicques ne moing curieulzes que plaisantes translatees de vieil gauloys en languaige de nostre temps."

2. Historiated *M* (fol. 3r). Scene inscribed in a gold-leaf frame ornamented at the corners with elongated cusps vaguely suggestive of stylized foliate decoration. The brown capital *M* floats within the scene. To the left is a house or castle; a male figure, in a black robe and hat, stands within the left portion of the *M*, a female in a reddish-brown dress with a light (ermine?) over-blouse within the right section. The figures apparently represent Jehan's uncle (Oudart) and cousin (Remiette). The miniature presents an artificially undulating horizon, and the ground is provided with scattered sprigs of vegetation. The ground, hills, and house are done in the same gray that is used in the miniature on fol. 1r; the sky uses the same dull blue.

3. Historiated *O* (fol. 9r). The initial is again set in the scene, and the whole miniature is set in a simple, square gold-leaf frame. Within the *O* a figure dressed in black is standing or walking in a town street, facing away from the viewer; the placement in the text suggests that this is the Jewess. At right is a large house with an overhanging second floor; at left are three houses (although four shadows on the street suggest that an additional house may be obscured by the capital *O*). The moon and stars are visible, and a large bird or bat flies near the figure. The street, which is a pale gray, merges gradually into the darker gray of the sky; there is no horizon.

4. Historiated *L* (fol. 17v) in gold, within the scene. The miniature is surrounded by a disk molding, a red frame decorated by small bezants or gold disks connected with one another by straight black lines. A crudely painted figure of a woman in blue, with a white apron, stands at right, holding a crock or pitcher. A well is located in the lower center. (Clearly, this miniature depicts Pasquette, who uses her trip to the well as an excuse to visit her aunt and provide her with information regarding the plot against Jehan; see fol. 30v.) Above the initial is a church, and houses stand on either side. Again there is no horizon shown, the ground merging into the sky. Blue, gray, and brown predominate, but the initial and frame make this the most colorful of the miniatures.

5. Historiated *P* (fol. 20r) in gold inside a square gold frame. The space between the frame and the letter is filled with simple green foliage. Within the capital is a head and shoulders portrait of a man, his features crudely drawn. The colors are brown and gray.

The miniatures, which date quite obviously from the nineteenth century, were executed by an artist of quite modest gifts. Certain of the features we might criticize in his work are doubtless due to the small scale of all but the first painting. The person in no. 3 is a rather lumpy, "snowman" figure composed of three round segments draped in a black robe. In no. 4, the equally small figure (only some two lines high) has no facial features, and the feet are indicated by mere spots of black paint. The small size of these paintings may in part explain the rather rudimentary technique, especially in the drawing of human figures and other small details of the miniatures; even the most charitable observor, however, is unlikely to be impressed with the artist's skill.

More significant are matters of perspective and proportion. I have already noted the curious situation in the full-page miniature, with its realistic perspective in the floor and spatial distortions elsewhere. That same miniature has a figure with elongated, clumsily drawn hands. No. 2 shows a figure (the male) with an elongated arm which, were it straightened, would reach to or below the knee. The size of figures, in proportion to their background, is frequently exaggerated.

The predominant colors of the miniatures are rather somber grays, blues, and browns, but these colors are relieved by the liberal use of gold and some red. (The illuminated initials, on the other hand, are for the most part done in rather lively colors, and there is abundant use of red, blue, and gold in small initials and other ornaments, making the manuscript extremely colorful, in marked contrast to the rather drab full-page miniature.) The paint of the miniatures is applied heavily, especially in the full-page scene, where there is a very large area filled with muddy gray (this is, in fact, the most interesting, yet finally least successful, of the miniatures). The use of short strokes extends even to the execution of straight lines, which appear to be drawn quite painstakingly. And wherever textures, folds, etc. are indicated (as in the details of the robe in no. 1), they seem to have been produced by similarly awkward painting, if not actual tracing. The results are competent but self-conscious and unimpressive paintings. Such features as the contrasting indications of perspective leave us with the unsettling notion that portions of the miniatures may have been imitated, if not copied, from similar miniatures elsewhere, whether painted or in the form of woodcuts or drawings.[7]

Such reservations about the miniatures arise when we examine them to assess their technique or artistic value. But it must be noted at the same time that, if we consider them as ornaments in the manuscript as a whole, they are successful in providing visual appeal and illustrating significant events or characters of the story. Despite their artistic flaws, they are fascinating decoration, and they (along with the other nineteen illuminated initials) contribute effectively to the creation of a work which undeniably presents considerable interest and charm.

C. Language

What follows is by no means a complete language study. Rather, it is a brief listing of some selected aspects of the language of the *Jehan Coquault.* My primary purpose is to demonstrate that the language is indeed sixteenth-century French—and relatively good sixteenth-century French at that. I have thus chosen to record a number of characteristic and revealing features of the language, without attempting to construct an exhaustive technical description of it.[8]

We should begin, however, with one detail concerning the date. In general, the syntactic and morphological features of the text appear to be from the earlier part of the sixteenth century; yet, the text contains a good number of vocabulary items that came into the language at various times during that century—some early, quite a few from the middle of the century, and some from as late as 1585. A few examples, chosen more or less at random, are: *affrioler* (1530), *pantois* (1534), *cagout* (1537), *mignardise* (1539), *pretexte* (1549), *debrouiller* (1549), *matoiz* (1578), *pigeonner* (1585). I have found in the text no words that entered the language after the end of the century.[9] I shall return later to the apparent disparity between vocabulary and other linguistic features.

The vocabulary is significant not only for the words that entered the French language during the sixteenth century, but also for those that either disappeared or changed meaning after that century. The examples in the manuscript are far too numerous to list fully; they include *angelot, dehait, enhorter, existimer, estrif, haim, prou,* and literally dozens, if not hundreds, of others.

Phonologically, the language presents most of the features we would expect, especially fairly early in the century. For example, the alternation of ε with *oi* (or *ei*) is usual. The pronunciation of *oi* changed from a diphthong to wε (often written *oe* or *oue*); in frequent instances, moreover, the *w* disappeared. Thus, the *Coquault* presents both *voire* ("truly, in truth") and *vere;* also *veez (=voyez)* and *veoirés.* That the *w* was still sounded in many cases is indicated by the forms *tirouer* and *tiroer, coueffes, dressouer, aclinouer.* Unexpectedly, the text also has *avor (=avoir)* and *bore (=boire).* Although we might anticipate *aver* and *bere,* the disappearance of the second element of the *oi* diphthong would be most unusual and suggests that these forms may be scribal errors.

Not surprisingly, the text consistently offers third-person plural preterites (first conjugation) in *-arent* rather than *-erent.* This phenomenon, due to the opening of ε to *a* before *r,* is represented by *recommencearent, entrarent, alarent,* and numerous others. These preterites were common in the early sixteenth century, but by late in the century they had become unusual and dialectal (see Brunot, II, 338). A related feature that merits note here is the presence of *armare* and *fare* (alongside *armaire* and *faire*). Henri Estienne notes on several occasions the general confusion of *a* and *e,* especially before *r.* Once the diphthong *ai* was reduced to ε, that sound could open to *a* as with the preterites noted, or as in *darenieres, guarir,* etc. Whether followed by *r* or not, the alternation of *a* and *ai* is not uncommon in the manuscript: *amee* and *amé, agu, declairer, regaigna.* The scribe once writes *bazé,* but alongside numerous examples of *baizer, baizé,* that form may be an error.

Before the sound **ʒ**, the manuscript presents *ai* consistently in cases where Modern French offers *a: mariaige, voisinaige, menaige, envisaigé, visaige, bruvaiges,* etc.

Other significant phonetic phenomena presented by the manuscript include the following alternations:

1. *o/ou: aprouvisionner, cousté, clouse, mourceaux, pouche, goubelet;* but *cropion, povés, esprové.* The manuscript has both *proupoz* and *propos.*

2. *e/eu.* In numerous cases, *e* and *eu* alternate freely, especially when pretonic: *treuver* is the usual form in the manuscript, but we also have *treva, trevoit;* also *beveter* for the more common *beuveter.* Occasionally, *e* occurs for *eu* when tonic as well: *vefve, mebles* (but also *meubles*).

3. *ou* for Modern French *eu,* and vice versa: *plourer, demourera; treuver, treuvant.*

4. *ui* for Modern French *i: vuida, vuidé.*

5. *ei* for Modern French *e* [ə] *(meiner)* or for *i (seigner).*

Nasal *o* was very close to a nasal *u* in sixteenth-century French, and it is so indicated in the *Coquault: lung, numbre, ungants, unze. En* and *an* are interchangeable signs of the nasal *a: attendent* (present participle), *menger, anfant.*

R was a relatively unstable phonetic element in Middle French, despite the insistence of grammarians that it be always pronounced. The sound tended to drop, for example, when final or when preceded by a plosive and followed by final *e.* When silent, it was still generally written—but not invariably, as witness the forms (cited by Gougenheim, pp. 30-31) *paller(=parler), calende (=calendre),* the rhyme *sapphiz/filz,* etc. See also Brunot, II, 270-2. Forms in which the *r* is lacking in the Spencer manuscript include *cueu* (for *cueur), toujous, Oudat (*for *Oudart), reguad (*for *reguard).* The manuscript offers three instances of *voste* (although these may be simple scribal omissions, since we also have a good number of *vostre*).

Final *s* was generally silent before a consonant (except at a pause). The scribe writes *tandi, quellesque, jambe* (as plural), *coing* (also plural).

The manuscript presents a limited number of grammatical forms that require note here. There are numerous occurrences of *on (=ou,* an old contracted form of *en le;* cf. feminine *en la).* This form, which appears in Rabelais, quickly becomes rare and archaic; see Brunot, II, 277. The plural is *es.*

The plural of nouns is generally formed by *-s.* However, *-z* occurs frequently, especially after a consonant: *esperitz, decretz, oeuilz.*

The equivalent of Modern French *grande* (fem.) is, as expected, *grant;* the adverbial form is *grantement.*

Regarding verbs, I have already noted *amé* (from the early infinitive *amer).* In the present indicative, the first person singular rarely has *-s: veoys* is present, but otherwise *doib, ay, suy, fay, rend, sceay, vay, veid* and *void.* The singular or familiar imperative varies freely in its use of *-s: humette, conte, lesse, dy,* but *entres, estudies, espies.* Similarly, the formal or plural imperative exists without *s* in *cuidé,* with *s* in *notés, croyés.*

Sixteenth-century French offers first-person singular imperfects and conditionals in *-oie, -oi, -ois* (or *-oye,* etc.). *-Oye* is most common in the *Coquault,* as witness *avoye, tentoye, departiroye,* etc. However, the less usual form in *-oi* or *-oy* also occurs: *parloy, vouldroi, dormoy, mouroi.* In the conditional, the manuscript offers the forms *fairois, fairoit,* rather than *ferois, feroit:* this was relatively common, although it was not approved by the grammarians of the period (see Brunot, II, 361-2). In addition, we have *farai,* which doubtless represents a phonological phenomenon noted above: the opening of *e* to *a* before *r.*

Miscellaneous forms that deserve note are *dont* and *dond,* forms that disappear (as conjunctions) later in the century; *ne...ne,* which give way to *ni...ni* during the period; *nenny,* which is common only in the first half of the century; *tresque,* rare by the end of the period; *ne...grain,* which disappears from literary vocabulary; *anui*[*t*], *atant, l'autrier, tresttout*—all of which become increasingly unusual in the course of the sixteenth century.

In general, the syntax presents few surprises. Tense sequence conforms rather closely to the modern order. In some instances, the text offers a future where we could expect an imperative in Modern French. Most genders are as in Modern French; exceptions are *la reste* (usual in the sixteenth century) and *une huis* (a probable scribal error). *Coemitiere* is masculine in the manuscript, as in Modern French; it was most often feminine in the sixteenth century, but both genders are attested.

Subjunctives also correspond, in the main, the modern usage: "a ceste fin que ayez," "vous playse" (though without *que*—a common sixteenth-century structure), "prie nostre divin Saulveur que il vous doinst," "ne cuyde moy que soyez," etc.

The manuscript presents two systems of demonstratives, and their usage corresponds to customary sixteenth-century practice: *celluy, icelluy, icelle, iceulx* can be used both adjectivally and pronominally, whereas *cest, cestuy, ceste, ces* are present only as adjectives.

The relative *que* is twice used as a subject (in the place of Modern French *qui).* This is not abnormal in the period; it was originally a neuter, the use of which was extended in Middle French to the feminine and, occasionally, to the masculine. See Pope, par. 864.

Prepositions are most often used as in Modern French, although there are certain cases in which they are omitted before an infinitive: "ne pouvoit se saouler contempler . . ."

By far the most common and distinctive syntactic feature of the text, in terms of word order, is the postposed subject pronoun. In many cases, as is to be expected, the subject pronoun is simply omitted; for example: "Or sçavés trop bien que. . ." When it is not omitted, however, it is generally placed after the verb and is most often put in the disjunctive form. This usage is not rare in the sixteenth century, and the pronoun was regularly postposed in certain situations (e.g., impersonal expressions, sentences beginning with *aussi,* etc.). Not infrequently, the subject pronoun then appeared in the disjunctive form, where it was apparently felt to be in apposition with the unexpressed conjunctive form of the subject. In the *Coquault,* however, this is the normal structure: "ne cuyde moy que soyez en dangier de mort . . ." In a few cases, both pronouns (conjunctive and disjunctive) are present: "Ne veulx je moy mectre . . . ."

It should be noted that the *cuyde moy, vay moy* structure is used primarily in conversation and that, moreover, it occurs virtually not at all in the prologue and epilogue. These facts may lead us to suspect that the structure is not part of the author's own language, but rather an indication of the characters' conversational style, perhaps even of their provincial origin. But it is also possible, whether the text is a sixteenth-century creation or a translation, that the syntax is designed to give it an archaic character and tone, thereby providing apparent corroboration of the claim that the narrator found an earlier text and rendered it *en langaige plus nouveau.* Unfortunately, the beginning and ending sections of the text are too brief to permit us to test adequately the impression that this syntactic pattern does not extend to those sections. Yet, the notion of a translator putting a text into a deliberately archaic language would explain the disparity between the rather late vocabulary, on the one hand, and the numerous features of the text that identify the language as belonging to the earlier part of the sixteenth century.

Whatever the reason for this disparity, the fact remains that the manuscript presents a language that is clearly and obviously of the sixteenth century. There are some linguistic curiosities, but there are no features which might not occur in a manuscript of the time. Many of the departures from a "standard" language of the period represent, in fact, an orthography, a syntax, and a morphological system which, quite expectedly, are far from fixed. Grammarians of the period disagreed on everything from genders to verb endings, and texts were less uniform even than theory. Consequently, it would be surprising if the manuscript of the *Jehan Coquault* did *not* present a number of irregularities. In any event, we have no linguistic cause to doubt that the literary text preserved in our nineteenth-century manuscript was in existence three centuries earlier.

D. Source

Substantial problems remain concerning the period and circumstances of the *Coquault's* original composition. As I have suggested, the codex itself was executed during the nineteenth century, and probably in the later part of that period; the immaculate condition of the vellum, the hand and spacing of the written text, and especially the illuminations and miniatures attest to that.[10] But what was the forger's source? The manuscript might be an exact copy of an earlier work, or it might represent a skillful forger's adaptation of an antecedent text.[11] But in either case, it is unclear whether the original was medieval or later.

I have found no text on which the *Coquault* might be based.[12] Under the circumstances, it is not easy to evaluate the claim (fol. 2v) that the text is translated from Old French. Internal evidence, drawn from an analysis of narrative matter, is of relatively little use in any attempt to identify the original date of composition. Nonetheless, two of the most striking narrative features of the *Istoyre* might profitably be noted here.

First, there is the love potion concocted by Remiette, to be given to Jehan. The recipe is provided her by La Sagotte, a sorceress. Medieval manuals of sorcery, known as *grimoires,* contain a good deal of information on potions and brews, and certain of the elements of this recipe are demonstrably authentic. For example, one medieval example calls for three pubic hairs and three hairs from the left armpit.[13] Those ingredients, along with three hairs from the head, are part of Remiette's potion. Other traditional methods and materials often noted are drawings made on parchment, the use of new porcelain bowls, and containers that have been thoroughly washed and tightly corked; those elements, too, are found in the *Istoyre.* Moreover, menstrual blood, used in La Sagotte's recipe, is known to be a common ingredient, [14] although I have not found elsewhere the peculiar details about collecting it (see fol. 31v-32r). In other words, if our sixteenth-century writer were inventing rather than translating, he evidently had sound knowledge of such details as the recipe for a medieval love potion. But whether the original author was medieval or later cannot be known.

The details regarding the Jews in the story are also significant, though (again) not conclusive. Early beliefs are well-documented: Jews were considered by many to be "ugly, malodorous, animal-like."[15] In the *Coquault*, accordingly, townspeople are convinced that the Jewess is hideously ugly, with long claws and a nose similar to an owl's beak, and that she emits an odor of sulphur. We later learn that this family of Jews came from the Caucasus, a detail that may recall the medieval notion that the Ottoman invaders were Jews.[16] Like the recipe for the love potion, the details regarding the Jews could be medieval, but they might also demonstrate no more than the writer's familiarity with traditional beliefs—and, in this case, beliefs that did not disappear with the Middle Ages.

Neither the material discussed here nor other narrative elements (nor, for that matter, the language) will permit us to assign the original composition of the *Cronicques* to a specific time. It is not impossible that the sixteenth-century writer fabricated the notion of an Old French text that required translation; similar claims have been made by numerous writers. On the other hand, we have no persuasive reason to doubt that claim, and the work may, indeed, be from a soiled and rotting manuscript composed in Old French, discovered and modernized during the sixteenth century, and recorded by our forger three hundred years later.

Fortunately, the uncertainty regarding the composition of the work does not detract from the interest of the manuscript itself, an artfully executed product of the nineteenth-century fascination with an earlier age. Nor does that uncertainty lessen the value of the story *as story,* and, as the following essay will demonstrate, the *Istoyre de Jehan Coquault* is an engaging and charming tale. It merits—and will reward—our attention, whatever its date.

II. THE STORY

The *Jehan Coquault* is a story of deceit, seduction, anti-semitism, sorcery, blackmail, and infanticide; there is, in other words, hardly a lack of intrigue and action. In its main outlines, however, the story is deceptively direct, uncomplicated, and linear in its development. In fact, it takes very few words to summarize it. When Jehan Coquault's mother dies, his uncle (Oudart) and his beautiful cousin (Remiette) conspire to separate him from his inheritance. Their attempts are foiled by the stratagems of Father Anthoine. Once the priest has saved the young man from his uncle and cousin, he finds him a bride, a beautiful Jewess whom he has just succeeded in converting.

Reduced to such an outline, the story may sound less than fascinating. Yet the effective presentation of the characters, the appeal of the strong story line, and the economy of the author's narrative method all work together to produce a work of considerable interest. It is, as I suggested earlier, not only a historical and textual curiosity, but also a well-constructed narrative, a very good story that deserves to be known and read.

All the characters in the work (with the debatable exception of Anthoine) are fundamentally one-dimensional, but they are clearly and strongly drawn, and they serve the author's purposes well. Jehan's uncle Oudart has a single desire (the acquisition of money, specifically Jehan's money) and no scruples in regard to his method of acquisition. Remiette is notable for a similar lack of scruples and for her lascivious behavior. Nor is she very discriminating: she prefers the young man who periodically climbs through her bedroom window, but she is quite ready (when asked) to exercise her particular skills on Jehan.

Pere Anthoine is somewhat more complex than the others. His motives, in contrast to those of Remiette and Oudart, are above reproach, but his methods are as unscrupulous as theirs. In Jehan's interest, Anthoine shrinks neither from bribery nor from blackmail. Moreover, the priest appears to take an almost malicious pleasure in deception—even in deceiving Jehan for no apparent purpose, when he conceals from him the identity of the Jewess. Initially, of course, there *is* a reason for the deception, for she is yet unconverted. But even after her conversion has removed the obstacle to their union, Anthoine comments, in playful ignorance, that he cannot see how a relationship between a Christian and a Jew could possibly work. Jehan, less gullible than usual, remarks that Anthoine would not have brought him to her unless he had a solution to that problem; only then does the priest explain that the lady is no longer Jewish.

In Anthoine's ethical world, the end justifies the means. He can lead Le Brenou to drink, he can blackmail La Sagotte, he can bribe, threaten, and deceive—and all these actions are compatible with his religious role, simply because they are in Jehan's interest. Of course, for Oudart and Remiette, the end similarly justifies the means, but they have the misfortune not to be on God's side—or Jehan's, or the narrator's. In fact, when Anthoine schemes, the narrator goes so far as to praise him, noting (fol. 15v) that he has *l'esperit ne moing bon que agu;* when Oudart and Remiette do the same, they are characterized simply as a *ruzé matoiz* and a *ruzee pute.*

Jehan is Candide. He is of course the center of the drama, but he serves primarily as a foil for the others, doing little except following Anthoine's instructions. Although he has some experience in dealing with family business matters, he is irremediably deficient in all other kinds of experience. In spite of his mother's warning, he naively continues to trust his relatives—until Anthoine eventually reveals all to him. It is his cousin who initiates him into erotic pleasures, when "...luy jecta les bras au col et apliqua ses lebvres moites sus sa bouche, en la quelle fourra sa langue grillante et endemenee..." (34r). This kiss, we are told, awoke in him "un sentiment tout nouveau" (35v)—apparently equal measures of wonder, surprise, and basic sexual arousal—and "luy fouettoit le sang" (36r). The naive, wide-eyed manner in which he responds to erotic pleasures marks all his reactions: to the revelations made by Anthoine, to the beauty of the Jewess, and to all the ordinary and extraordinary things and events of the work. He is a character to whom things happen, not a character who, himself, does very much. While the story revolves around him, he does not shape it. For the most part, he does not act (except to follow instructions): he reacts. He is, in other words, the calm and consistently uncomprehending center of the storm of intrigue around him.

I have begun with a survey of the characters because it is ultimately from them that the story develops. The outcome of that story is of course preordained, but it is less the narrator than the characters themselves who determine its direction.[17] For example, because Oudart is "l'home le plus convoiteux, cault, et ruzé que feut on pays" (5r), it is scarcely surprising that he mistreats his servant (Pasquette) or that, as a result, she wants to leave his employ and is moreover willing to spy on him. Immediately after her aid is enlisted by Anthoine, there is a corresponding passage in which the priest talks with Le Brenou, who long ago was threatened by La Sagotte, the sorceress he works for, after he saw her murder her own baby. He reveals that since that time he (like Pasquette) has been badly treated, that he would like to leave La Sagotte, and that for some time he has wanted to tell all. Anthoine skillfully takes advantage of the knowledge he gains from the two servants and is able to defeat Jehan's relatives. The priest is both clever and ruthless, but ultimately he is only a catalyst, setting in motion the forces that allow his opponents' evil character and motives to bring upon themselves the ruin predicted by the author.

In terms of its form, the story of Jehan's fortunes and misfortunes exhibits a simple but effective symmetry. In the beginning, the narrative rapidly introduces and prepares the drama, proceeding almost day by day, with the ending of a number of sections corresponding to nightfall or bedtime. However, once the intrigue is thoroughly developed, there comes a narratively static period, and we are told only that about a month passed. During this period, we have no details, but we know that Anthoine is busy gathering information and evidence (". . . amassoit de toutes parts," 27v). About the same time, Oudart reassesses his strategy. Becoming more desperate, he forgoes his attempts to arrange for Jehan to marry Remiette and capitalizes on his daughter's access to sorcery and her skills at seduction. Soon afterward (and, notably, in the very middle of the work), the narrative action begins anew, picks up its earlier pace, and proceeds uninterrupted to the dénouement. Thus, the structure of the work, while far from complex, is pleasingly balanced. It offers a prologue and an epilogue, within which are an introduction and a conclusion. These frame the development of the intrigue and its resolution, which in turn embrace a static central section, a dramatically effective pause that permits information to be collected, forces marshalled, and strategy revised, before the story begins to move quickly toward its end.

However, once we look at it more attentively, that story proves to be considerably less simple than either the form or my earlier synopsis might suggest. First of all, the primary thematic concern of the work is not (as it initially appears to be) the disposition of Jehan's inheritance, but rather the process by which he finds a wife. This concern appears early, as Oudart discusses Jehan's marriage prospects with the young man's mother before her death (5v-6r); he suggests that Jehan and Remiette are perfect for each other. Discussing the same matter with Jehan, his mother later expresses her reservations about Remiette as a prospective bride and urges Jehan to consult Anthoine about everything, but especially about marriage. Oudart does of course want to relieve Jehan of his money, but his first choice of methods is to persuade Jehan to marry Remiette; he broaches this subject immediately after the funeral of Jehan's mother, while the young man's grief is still so great that he cannot eat. Jehan's marriage is also a preoccupation of Anthoine, who assures the youth more than once that he will find him a wife. In fact, Jehan appears less concerned than anyone else with his own marriage—until he sees the Jewess and is consumed by love. Even the author adds his comments on this subject, remarking that when Jehan was about twenty, he lacked nothing except a wife to complete his happiness.

In developing his themes, the author makes frequent use of a system of "suspended references"—a series of allusions, events, or characters that are mentioned but temporarily left unexplained or partially explained. They appear to be loose threads, but once we reach the end of the work and are able to see the full design of the work, it is clear that the threads were not loose at all. The first such reference is a casual remark made by Jehan when his mother asks him for assurance that he will not marry his cousin if he finds any trace of dishonesty or sin in her. He replies that, in such a case, he would rather marry the Jewess. The author soon interrupts to explain this reference to a member of a reviled and mistrusted local family (the Jewess is thought to have claws and a nose like an owl's beak, and it is common knowledge that these Jews emit a strong sulphurous odor). We learn that it had become customary in the area for people to express their opinion of any distasteful task or duty by exclaiming: "I'd rather marry the Jewess." At this point, the narrator drops the subject and returns to Jehan and his mother, with only the length of the passage (nearly five pages, or two and one-half folios) suggesting that the expression or the Jews it refers to might play a later role in the work.

The same comment (". . . espoulzeroie plus tost la Juifve!") is made later, and we find various other references to the Jewess, references that occur with increasing frequency in the work. A single example is a rumor, intended as slander and later found to be correct, to the effect that Anthoine has been seen entering the Jewess's house.

The most significant fact about the references to her is that they all prove to be predictions—and predictions that are realized at the end of the work. Jehan has twice asserted that he would rather marry the Jewess than his cousin (first in recognition of the possibility of Remiette's lack of virtue, later in reaction to proof of that lack). Early in the work, Jehan's mother defends the Jews[18] and tells him that we should all pray that God convert the Jewess to Christianity; that is also, of course, Anthoine's purpose in going to her home, and he is at last successful. Finally, when Jehan confronts his cousin with his knowledge of her plot, she swears that she will get revenge and will do so in such a way that Jehan will never be able to find any wife except the Jewess.

At the end, it is clear that there have been no gratuitous references in the work. God and Anthoine have indeed converted the Jewess (whose name is Noémi), and this event permits the other predictions to be fulfilled: Jehan prefers to marry the Jewess, and he does. Remiette's treachery and lack of virtue, on the other hand, assure that her threat will be realized: Jehan will indeed have no other woman than Noémi as his wife.

Thus, all the comments about the Jews, whether spoken in anger, in slander, or (as in Jehan's case) in the innocent use of a local idiom, point ultimately toward the young man's marriage and the dénouement of the story. The point at which the reader becomes aware of their purpose is a matter of some conjecture and of individual reader reaction. Certainly, our awareness comes gradually. We may begin to suspect something as soon as the narrator goes out of his way to explain the first reference to the Jews; otherwise, that reference seems to be a casual allusion. Little by little, however, the repeated allusions create the correct impression that the Jewess is a central, major force in the work. Until she finally appears in person, near the end of the text, she is a major "absent" character, invisible yet able to shape the work without being physically present in it. She provides a recurring theme and a structure of expectation, of anticipation and ultimate realization. This initially secondary narrative structure slowly develops, asserts its prominence, merges with the story of Jehan's uncle and cousin, and eventually supplants the latter as the primary narrative focus of the work. This development is gradual and subtle, yet it has been pre-ordained by the author and by his narrative "rules," and it has been foreseeable, if not necessarily foreseen, from the beginning.

All the themes finally converge, as I suggested, and all the ends are tied up. In this regard, we should note one small but significant sub-plot that is skillfully interwoven with the primary narrative. Late in the work, Anthoine promises that he will find Jehan a wife, but the young man responds that he wants only the one who helped him and who (as the priest insists) is a creation of Jehan's dreams. Soon afterwards, Jehan visits his mother's grave and becomes curious about the identity of the person who has placed flowers on it; thus an apparently new theme is abruptly introduced. While at the cemetery, he enters a church and asks God to help him find the woman of his dream. Returning to Anthoine, Jehan asserts again that he will marry no lady except *"icelle de mon songe"* (49v); Anthoine responds by suggesting that they change the subject, whereupon the youth asks about the source of the flowers on the grave. He learns that they were left there by a woman, *belle comme ung ange* (50r), frequently maligned by others but defended by his mother. Anthoine agrees to take Jehan to meet and thank her, and, without subtlety, he tells Jehan that, if she pleases him, he may feel free to ask for her in marriage. Thus does Jehan meet the lady of his dreams, the lady who covered his mother's grave with flowers, and the Jewess—all in one.

Strictly speaking, the plot does not require the theme of the flower-strewn grave. If Noémi was ready to convert (as we soon learn), it would suffice for Anthoine to reveal to Jehan that she is not a dream; the two young people could easily have been united. But if this subsidiary theme is dispensable, it is nonetheless narratively effective. First of all, it establishes Jehan's mother as a significant character (who dies at the beginning of the work, as the Jewess is a major character who does not appear until the end). The mother's prayers and supplications to prayer doubtless play a role in converting Noémi (with Anthoine as the agent) and making her thereby an acceptable bride for Jehan. At the same time, the mother's charitable attitude toward the Jewess, who "n'en est pas moing une creature de Dieu" (8r), eventually draws Noémi to the grave and enables Jehan to find her. Thus, the flowers on the grave do serve a particular purpose. The scene creates additional dramatic interest, but it also recalls the beginning of the work, emphasizes the mother's influence on the ultimate conclusion, and establishes charity as the dominant force in the drama—a force that can foil the most fiendish of plots.

Shaping and moving the characters and story, the narrator leaves nothing to chance. References, apparently gratuitous, are in fact significant. And in his zeal to see us properly through the work, he becomes both our guide and our confidant. He advises us ("sometimes things don't work out as we would like; it's better to trust in divine providence," 4v); he explains patiently ("now I must tell you . . .," "now I will return to . . ."); he frequently uses plurals to join us as observors or to draw us into complicity with him ("comme savons . . ."). He shares with us the reactions of others,[19] the characters' intentions,[20] and his own views. He does not even resist explicit editorial commentary, describing Jehan's relatives, as I noted earlier, in no uncertain terms *(ruzé matoiz* and *ruzee pute)* and noting that, however badly beaten Oudart might be, we must not pity him, "car en avoit luy merité bien d'advantaige" (42r).

Not least among the narrative and rhetorical resources used to engage and beguile the reader is the author's considerable wit, particularly in brief observations and asides. He has an obvious taste for the "one-liner," the pithy observation that often has an almost epigrammatic quality. We are told, for example, that La Sagotte, who lived the life of a *vraye pute,* found it far better to work with her rump than with her hands (". . . bien meilleur laborer du cropion que des doigtz," 22r). When Anthoine wants to lubricate Le Brenou's tongue with alcohol, the latter notes that wine is always in far shorter supply than thirst (20v). After La Sagotte recites to Anthoine the recipe for the love potion (including candle wax, hair, and menstrual blood), he tells her: "That's a hellish stew [*ragoust d'enfer*], and I'll certainly never have you cook for me!" (32r). And after the death of Jehan's mother, the author indicates the hypocrisy of Oudart and Remiette by noting that, at dinner, their sorrow did not immobilize their jaws (12v-13r). In other words, the narrator leaves nothing unexplained, but his explanations and comments are invariably effective, either in elucidating character and plot or simply in providing amusing badinage and humor.

But in telling all, the narrator does not tell too much. On the contrary, his literary esthetic calls for us (as well as him) to be omniscient, at least in regard to the intrigue against Jehan. For a full appreciation of the story, in fact, it is essential that we know just what is planned and intended—and it is similarly essential that Jehan remain oblivious to it. In a work where a character's destiny is predictable and clearly controlled, it is natural for the narrator to be very visible and very obtrusive. And his technique consistently places us in a position to appreciate better the developing events around Jehan and to see the real extent to which Jehan himself controls nothing and understands little.

It would be a mistake to try to present the *Istoyre* as an extraordinary masterpiece of narrative art. It is not. But neither, on the other hand, is it a clumsy or unimaginative composition. The characters are rather simple and unsophisticated literary creations, but that is precisely what their role and the nature of the work dictate. The narration is for the most part very economical and effective, and the various elements of the plot are expertly interwoven. The primary appeal of the work is the most basic one possible: the simple desire to know "what happens next." The author appears to direct all his efforts and resources toward this end, toward the creation of suspense and anticipation. If those are indeed his goals, he succeeds admirably; the *Istoyre* is both engrossing and charming, and the work, as I suggested in the beginning, is art, no less than antique.

III. EDITORIAL PROCEDURES

Editorial treatment of this text is for the most part straightforward, but there are a good number of problematical cases. Many of the problems concern internal inconsistencies which might be due either to the state of sixteenth-century French (in which case the reading should normally stand) or to the scribe's tendency toward carelessness (which should be corrected). For example, he often omits the second of two vowels; that is almost certainly what happened with *bore* and *vorre* (for *boire* and *voirre* [=*verre*]), but the situation is less clear with *bazé* and *fare,* two forms that are theoretically possible, although other instances of *baizé* and *faire* in the text suggest that they may be of scribal origin.

Two other brief examples of editorial difficulties will suffice for the present (others are discussed in the notes following the critical text). The scribe twice writes *va moy* + verb. In fact, *va* is a possible, albeit rare, form when the subject is *moy* (see Gougenheim, p. 223). In one other case, we find *va* as a first-person form when the subject is not expressed. Secondly, the manuscript has *retire* (19v) and *cerche* (41v) where we would expect infinitives. There are a number of attested instances of confusion between infinitives and past participles (see Brunot, who cites *veult demouré,* II, 271), and perhaps we should see these forms as *retiré* and *cerché,* although the phenomenon does not occur elsewhere in the manuscript. How should the editor deal with such questions?

I have rejected as excessively conservative the notion that any remotely possible form should escape emendation. I have taken it instead as my function to facilitate the reading of the work, and thus I have emended a number of readings (particularly orthographic and phonetic) that a traditional editor might defend. When in doubt, I have tended toward emendation. Needless to say, my emendations are always documented and frequently discussed. Fortunately, they are not so numerous as to clutter the text or to obscure its original flavor or appearance.

I thus emend *va* to *va*[*y*] in the examples noted above, and *retire* and *cerche* to *retire*[*r*] and *cerche*[*r*]. I also restore the final *s* to several plurals from which it is omitted, and to *tandi*[*s*] *que.* I emend *voste* three times, in accord with a dozen occurences of *vostre.*

The scribe, as I noted, tends to omit letters, nasal bars, etc. that are obviously required. I emend *bore* and *vorre,* as well as *bazé* (to *ba*[*i*]*zé*) but I leave *fare* and *armare* in recognition of the frequent alternation of *a* and *e* before *r.* I have also restored *r* in a number of words *(Oudat, reguad,* etc.*).* These are instances in which we might not be surprised to see *r* fall, but it happens only sporadically in this manuscript, and I am not persuaded that it is a characteristic of the author's or scribe's language. Again, the accessibility of the text is my primary concern, and consequently my emendations should not be taken as implying that all rejected readings are necessarily errors.

At the same time, I have no desire to restore the language to a sterile uniformity which early texts rarely exhibit. I have, for example, left *mouroi* and *dormoy,* two unusual but quite acceptable first-person imperfect forms, as well as similar conditionals. Also left without emendation are common phonetic variants *(treva* alongside *treuva, povoit* and *pouvoient)* and, of course, simple orthographic variations of the *seulement/seullement* variety.

The scribe is inconsistent in regard to spacing of words; he writes *pour ce que* and *pource que, neant moing* and *neantmoing, de hait* and *dehait.* Wherever the spacing is obvious, I follow the scribe and maintain the inconsistency; when it is not certain whether a division into two words is intended (e.g., when the space is slight or when a word is divided between two lines of text), I adopt the form that is most frequently present in the text. In two or three instances only, I disregard the scribe's spacing for the sake of clarity.

The abbreviations in the manuscript are for the most part simple and traditional. There are q̄ *(que),* q̇ *(qui), /Z(et),* 9 *(-us,* as *pl* 9*),* the nasal bar *(cõme* for *comme),* ꝑ *(pro-),* ℗ *(per, par, pour).* A question is raised by the abbreviation q̄ before a vowel (e.g., q̄*il,* q̄*y*). Normally, we might expect to resolve this abbreviation as *qu'* in such situations (thus, *qu'il*). However, when the scribe occasionally writes out the word, instead of abbreviating it, before vowels, he consistently offers *que;* e.g., *que une* (4r), *que a luy* (5r), *que ung* (12r), *que une* (42v), etc. It has thus seemed preferable in every case to resolve q̄ as *que.* The only exception in this regard is q̄*stoit* (which I expand as *qu'estoit,* 45v). In one instance, the scribe writes q̇*l* (rather than *que il* or q̄ *il*); I resolve the form as *qu'il* (25r).

The scribe uses no accents or diacriticals. Accents were of course used sporadically and inconsistently during the sixteenth century (see Pope, par. 735-7). Rather than try to duplicate an unpredictable system, I have used accents as sparingly as possible; furthermore, I have limited myself to the acute accent, which I use only to indicate pronunciation. Thus, I write *ruzè* but leave the feminine as *ruzee,* since the pronunciation of the latter form is clear. In the same way, an accent is used to discriminate between second-person singular and plural verbs: *(tu) parles, (vous) parlès.* However, an accent is not used on the plural verb if the ending is *-z* (following Dolet, Garnier, and others; see Brunot, II, 301).

It is sometimes impossible to distinguish *f* from "long" *s.* For example, 3v has either *vefve* or *vesve* (=veuve); both forms are attested in the sixteenth century (doubtless for the same reason: the difficulty of distinguishing the letters). I write *vefve,* assuming the influence of the masculine *veuf.*

I have resolved *i* and *j, u* and *v* according to modern usage. The scribe uses no punctuation; I have punctuated as necessary for clarity. He does, however, use a colored ornament to indicate the beginning of a new "paragraph." In general, my paragraph divisions tend to agree with his, but I have provided more divisions (especially in setting off quoted speech), and in some cases I have ignored his, when the sense of the text dictates it.

When I have considered it necessary to add letters or words, I have done so within brackets and (usually) without comment. Wherever I have, on the other hand, changed or deleted material, the original reading is listed in a note.

IV. NOTES TO INTRODUCTION

[1] *The Spanish Forger*, by William Voelkle, assisted by Roger S. Wieck (New York: The Morgan Library, 1978) is an attempt to catalogue all the known paintings of the Spanish Forger; Voelkle also offers a brief stylistic study of the Forger's work.

[2] For this reason I retain the term "forgery" in my subtitle only with some reservation; "counterfeit" might be a preferable designation. It might be noted that both of the "aging" techniques mentioned here were characteristic of the Spanish Forger. He regularly scraped the vellum (often removing portions of earlier texts); and the *craquelure* contributed, often persuasively, to the appearance of antiquity (but see Voelkle, p. 13). The only exception to my statement regarding the *Coquault* manuscript is a small amount of cracking in the paint of the tiled floor in the full-page miniature.

[3] Here and elsewhere, I use the term "medievalism" broadly, to include the sixteenth century as well as earlier periods. It is not at all clear that the forger or his patrons made finer distinctions than these, and the term will suffice for present purposes.

[4] See my note on "The Kansas Manuscript of *L'Istoire de Jehan Coquault*," *Manuscripta*, 25, No. 3 (1981), 172-6.

[5] I do not number the blank leaves; thus, in my edition, the beginning of the text is designated as fol. 1r, and the work extends to fol. 55v.

[6] The script presents some peculiarities of horizontal spacing. In addition, the scribe uses a curious "backwards" *y*, in which the left branch of the letter descends below the line and then turns to become an almost horizontal stroke to the right.

[7] Certain of the illuminated initials in the manuscript bear a striking resemblance to some capitals used in William Morris's Kelmscott Press publications. I would not contend that there is specific influence at work here, but Morris and the illuminator of the *Coquault* manuscript have nonetheless drawn from the same style of initial.

[8] Although I have consulted a variety of histories of the language, historical grammars, etc. in the preparation of the language study and the

textual notes, I have thought it useful to limit my specific references (given in the body of my discussions) primarily to Ferdinand Brunot, *Histoire de la langue française des origines à 1900. Tome II: Le Seizième Siècle* (Paris: Armand Colin, 1906), with occasional citations to Georges Gougenheim, *Grammaire de la langue française du seizième siècle* (Lyon, 1951) and Mildred K. Pope, *From Latin to Modern French* (Manchester, 1934, 1966).

[9]The one possible exception to this statement is *ayguerie,* on fol. 20r; see my note (no. 25) on this word. Standard etymological dictionaries frequently disagree, of course, about the earliest attested occurrence of a word (and some may give dates that differ from those offered for the words listed above). There is also some difference of opinion in regard to the words *ragoust* and *degoustant,* which appear in the *Coquault* and which may be from the sixteenth *or* the seventeenth century. However, the infinitive *degouster* dates from the 1530's, *ragouster* from the fourteenth century (in Froissart) and their root *goust* from earlier still. It is reasonable to assume that both *ragoust* and *degoustant* did indeed exist in the sixteenth century, and in any case, these questionable origins—and that of *ayguerie*—give us no reason to doubt that the work was either composed early or based on an early text.

[10]Contrary to early practice, the illuminator of the *Coquault* frequently applies gold leaf after other colors are in place. The gold leaf is always applied last on the small ornaments at the ends of lines, but for larger decoration (initials and miniatures), he is unpredictable. When the historiated initials themselves are gold (nos. 4,5), the gold appears to have been applied after the background but then outlined in black or in the background color.

[11]In theory, of course, there is another possibility: that a genuine early text has been decorated with modern miniatures and illuminations. Such a phenomenon was hardly rare (the Spanish Forger and others sometimes worked this way); however, this explanation appears to be excluded by the state of the vellum, the style of writing, etc. I am also excluding here, as I implicitly did above, a fourth possibility, which is that the work is a nineteenth-century invention: could any forger (or philologist, for that matter) have written a text of this length without committing serious blunders in a language three hundred years old?

[12]There is however a remarkable coincidence of names in a volume of *Mémoires* done by a certain Oudard Coquault of Reims during the seventeenth century (Jehan Coquault's uncle in the *Istoyre* is named Oudart, while the work takes place in Reims). Moreover, the Oudard of the *Mémoires* had a son

named Jean. Beyond these resemblances, however, the two works have nothing in common (the seventeenth-century text being a political and social memoir of the city). See *Mémoires de Oudard Coquault, Bourgeois de Reims (1649-1668),* ed. Ch. Loriquet (Reims, 1875).

[13]See Harry E. Wedeck, *Love Potions Through the Ages* (New York, 1963), p. 228.

[14]For example, Tinctoris in 1460 mentions an ointment (less appetizing even than La Sagotte's potion) that included menstrual blood and such additional ingredients as toads and the bones of exhumed corpses. See Jeffrey Burton Russell, *Witchcraft in the Middle Ages* (Ithaca: Cornell Univ. Press, 1972), p. 240; also Wedeck, p. 184.

[15]Venetia Newall, "The Jew as a Witch Figure," in *The Witch Figure,* ed. Venetia Newall (London: Routledge, 1973), p. 105.

[16]Newall, p. 107.

[17]And that direction is clear from the very beginning: we will see that "... comme l'homme de bon vouloir est touts jours guerdonné, oncques l'homme meschant ne peult eschapper on chastiment" (fol. 1v).

[18]She insists that all the rumors regarding the Jewess are only *bourdes et calumnies* and asserts that "ne debvons mauldire personne." She does however admit that the Jewess gives off a *trez fort odeur* (8v), commenting that she does not know whether it is sulphur of some other odor. Such statements, which corroborate one aspect of local prejudice, seem to compromise her defense of the Jewess. In fact, she is correct: we will later learn that Noémi wears a corset made of a leather that emits an *odeur trez fort et moult penetratif* (45r).

[19]For example, "l'on remarqua aiseement que les larmes de messyre Ouda[r]t et de sa fille n'estoient que cingeries et feintize" (12r).

[20]He announces, for instance, that Oudart, "... n'ayant peu trufer la mere, cuydoit bien soy s'en rescompenser avecques le filz" (12v).

L'ISTOYRE DE JEHAN COQUAULT

Antiennes cronicques ne moing curieulzes que plaisantes translatees de vieil gauloys en languaige de nostre temps

1r ANTIENNES CRONICQUES NE MOING CURIEULZES QUE
PLAISANTES TRANSLATEES DE VIEIL GAULOYS EN
LANGUAIGE DE NOSTRE TEMPS.[1]

1v   Si vouz supply, lecteur trez gratieux, recepvoir et agreer ces
cronicques, pource que ne les ay escriptes sinon a ceste seulle et unicque
fin de vouz ayder a eviter oysifveté, vouz rec[r]eer, et mectre toutes
melancholies hors de voz esperitz. Or se n'avés en dedaing de lire,
veoirés relateez en icelluy livre les istoyres ne moing curieulzes que
playsantes de Jehan Coquault et du grant Baya de Rains,[2] et cuidé moy
que ne regrecterés le temps despendeu a ceste lecture pour l'esbattement
que y aurés prins. Oultre plus, pourrés tirer des dictes cronicques
enseignement moult proufictable pource que y est clerement et appertement
monstré premier en l'istoyre de Jehan que comme l'homme de bon
vouloir est touts jours guerdonné, oncques l'homme meschant ne peult
2r   eschapper on chastiment. Par especial, veoirrés / en l'istoyre du grant
Baya comment avecques l'aide de Dieu et de Madame la Saincte Vierge, un
doul[c]ette, foible, mignotte, et gente pucelle defeit ung horrificque
monstre qui desoloit le pays pieça bien lung temps, et n'avoient peu faire
cela ne souldarts ne archiers, tant feussent attrempez, preux, de hault
cueur, et vaillantz en guerre—et notés que bonnes armes et munitions ne
leur faisoient faulte.

        Et a ceste fin que ayez toute fian[c]e es dictes cronicques, doib dire
dont les ay tirees: or ung jour que par fasson de passer le temps
m'amuzoye a grabeler ung tas de vieulx rolles issis de l'abbaye, treuvay
les dictes cronicques pesle-mesle avecques vieulx aultres parchemins,
dont n'avoye que faire pour le present, et croyés que n'est pas sans poyne
2v   que suy parveneu a les des- / brouiller et mectre en tel ordre que je vouz
les ofre en huy, pour ce que les dicts rolles estoient souillez, gastez, voire
mesme pourriz, en prou de pas d'advantaige l'escripture estoit tant
maulvaize que l'auriez prinse pour piedz de mousches. Et pour
complayre a touts entendementz, ay treuvé bon de translater ces istoyres
de vieil gauloy en langaige plus nouveau. Toutes foys ne regrecteray
point mon labeur se tant est que il aura peu vouz amuzer et recreer tant
seulement ung petit. Par ainsy, quand aurés leu, veu, et entendeu[3] mon
bon vouloir, vouz playse m'excuser et accorder mercy pour toutes
faultes, erreurs, ou obmissions.

A vouz et touts aultres qui liront, vouz fay trez humble reverence, et prie nostre divin Saulveur que il vous doinst sa grace en ce munde et son sainct paradiz en l'aul[t] re. *Amen.* /

3r   S'ENSUIT L'ISTOYRE DE JEHAN COQUAULT.[4]

Maulgré et envi tout bon vouloir, ne peulx je vouz affermer le milliaire de ces istoyres, pour ce que n'en ay peu descouvrir trasse aulcune es vielx rolles dont les ay extraictes; ains a la lection d'icelles[5] ung chascun veoira trop bien que doibvent elles[6] remonter a ung temps moult antien, ains n'en seront moing curieulzes pour aultant.

Ores je commence in nomine patris et filii et spiritus sancti, amen.

3v   En icelluy temps estoit en la cité / de Rains une haulte, preude, et noble dame moult cogneue et renommee pour sa pieté et ses bonnes oeuvres; aussy estoit elle amee et reveree de ung chascun. Or cest bonne dame estoit vefve de Messire André Coquault, homme de grant sapience et entendement, qui feut moult regrecté et plouré pour les grantz et leaulx services que avoit rendeus es charges de la jurisdiction; et quand trespassa le digne homme tant fust desolee la bonne dame et tant eust le cueur navré que l'auroit elle voulentier accompaigné en la tombe, s'elle n'eust eu de luy pour soulas ung filz chiery nommé Jehan.

Or n'est besoing de dire que la bonne mere benda son entendement et ses esperitz a nourir et eslever en l'amour et craincte de Dieu ce chier anfant, et pour attaindre telle fin apela a son ayde le Pere Anthoine, bon
4r   et / digne prebstre, antien amy de son defunct mary. Et estoit le dict prebstre moult amé et reveré on lieu, tant pour sa saincte coustume de vivre que pour sa haulte sapience. Aussy le jeune Jehan soubs tel maistre prouficta tant bien en tout que au dire de ung chascun ce estoit merveille.

Cependant, les annees passoient, et avoit luy ja attainct l'eage de vingt ans ou peu prez; finablement ne manquoit a luy que une compaigne pour parfaire son bon heur.

Or depuys son anfance Jehan souloit faire compaignie de une[7] cousine, fille du Sieur Oudart, veuf de Magdeleine Coqua[u]lt, soeur

de André Coquault, pere de Jehan. Et estoit existimee de ung chascun la
dicte Remiette Oudart (ainsy avoit elle nom) la plus gente et jolie pucelle
4v de toute la cité, voire mesme es environs, et toutz estoient / d'accord que
son union avecques son cousin Jehan fairoit le plus beau et convenant
mariaige que oncques feut faict en l'endroict. Finablement, tout paroissoit
presagier bon heur et liesse en ceste famille. (Souvent advient au rebour
de noz conjectures et soubhaictz; mieulx nouz en remectre aulx decretz
de la divine providence.)

COMMENT LA BONNE DAME COQUAULT FEUT PR[I]NSE PAR LA MALE FIEBVRE.

Par ainsy, les deux familles se hantoient frequentement, et n'estoit
entre elles nulles controversies, et Jehan atendoit patiemment l'heure de
marier sa belle cousine.

5r Or, cependant que l'on nourissoit Jehan en / tel espoir, son oncle
Oudart visoit a marier sa fille en aultre part que a luy, pourquoi cerchoit a
alicher ung jeune gars dont le pere estoit prisé trés riche au dyre de ung
chascun. Or notés que icelluy Oudart estoit l'home le plus convoiteux,
cault, et ruzé que[8] feut on pays, pourquoy lessoit le dict jeune gars
frequenter sa maizon soubs semblant de voisinaige. Ains ne demoura pas
lung temps sans estre acertainé que le pere du jeune homme oncques ne
bailleroi[t] consentement a icelluy mariaige; pourquoy retourna le dict
Oudart a Jehan (faulte de mieulx) et recommencea a parler a la dame
Coquault du mariaige des anfantz.

Ains, tout ainsy que telz affaires ne peulvent se concludre en ung
jour, les jours s'escouloient, voire mesme les moiz, quand la bonne dame
5v feut prinse d'une male fiebvre qui pieça lung temps desoloit / le pays; et
aulcuns—feussent jeunes ou vielx, riches ou povres—ne pouvoient s'en
deffendre, tant estoit maligne la dicte fiebvre. Or, cependant que la
maladie accravantoit et lessoit peu d'espoir ou point du tout, le
convoiteux Oudart s'en ala treuver la bonne dame et luy tint tel
languaige, ou peu prez:

"Chiere et honoree soeur, ne cuyde moy que[9] soyez en dangier de
mort, car combien que ceste fiebvre dont estes attaincte soyt moult
maulvaize, avés peu veoir que l'on peult en eschapper; non obstant cela,

est prudent mectre ordre en ses affaires. Or scavés trop bien que noz jeunes gentz s'aiment et que souventes foys entre nouz ha esté deliberé les unir, et sont ja eulx en eage conven[an]t par quoy en toute
6r   prouvoyance convient asseurer leur chevance encontre toute / male fortune, et fairiez saigement par bonne schedule me commectre l'administracion et goubvernement de l'hoirie de vostre filz, en attendent son mariaige avecques Remiette. Par ainsy, on cas que ne releviez de ceste maladie, ce faisant pourrés (se telle est la voulenté de Dieu) mourir sans craincte aulcune touchant l'advenir de vost[r]e[10] filz."

Atant se teut, et respondict la bonne dame:

"Chier, vouz rend graace et mercy pour vostre bon vouloir, ains n'ay je attendeu jusques a ceste heure pour mectre ordre es affaires de leans: jaçoit que Jehan soyt jeune d'eage, est ja bien apprins on goubvernement de menaig[e], et se par fortune estoyt empeschié en quoy que ce soyt, le bon Pere Anthoine ne luy fauldroyt on besoing."

6v   Avoir[11] entendeu cela et ne treuvant rien a obster, Oudart s'en/ala tout pantoys; toutes foys ne se reguarda comme batteu pour aultant, et se benda a attaindre ses visees en mectant en oeuvre engins, trainees, et tout.

COMMENT LA BONNE DAME COQUAULT ADMONESTA SON FILZ

Avoir bien pourpensé, envisaigé, et poisé son estat, veid trez bien la bonne dame ne avoir soy que peu de temps a vivre. Feist seoir son filz jouxte son lict, et l'admoneste comme s'ensuyt:

"Chier anfant, entends bien ces darenieres remonstrances, car void je moy clerement que soubs peu doib rendre mon aame a Dieu, et me departiroye je bien voulentier de ceste vie, n'estoit la poyne de te lesser
7r   seul. Neant- / moins, que la voulenté de Dieu soyt faicte. Par ainsy, ne demourera gueres que ne puisse plus t'ayder de mes semonces, car ne doib je meshuy conter les jours, ains les[12] heures. Lors, quand mes os seront soubz terre, ne fay faulte de te recorder mes darenieres parolles: premier, se oncques te veoidz empeschié en quoy que ce soyt, va incontinent requerir ayde et assistance du bon Pere Anthoine, car pour certain n'avons nouz eu meilleur amy, et chascune foy que feut ton pere a

requis de luy assistance s'en est touts jours moult bien treuvé. Ne fay entreprinse aulcune que n'ay[e] toy par advance prins conseil de luy—et par especial se estoyes toy en doubte de mariaige. Entendz bien, chier anfant, ja pleusieurs foys a esté deliberé entre ton pere et ton oncle
7v Oudart te marier avecqu[e]s ta cousine Remiette, sa / fille. Ne veulx je moy mectre empeschement aulcun a cela s'elle peult faire ton bon heur. Ains question de l'advenir de ses anfanz, une mere veoid bien loing; et jaceoit que la treuve moy moult gente et playsante, ne sceay pourquoy me suy je touts jours defié de elle et de ton oncle, et ay souvent pansé que luy convoitoit ta chevance, ains possible est que soye moy en erreur. Par ainsy, avant que rien concludre, prend bien toutes precaultions requises en tel pourchaz. Par especial, estudies et espies bien les moeurs et inclinacion[s] de ta cousine, et se par advanture descouvroyes en elle ung rien contraire a honnesteté et vertu, lesse la sans targement aulcun. Ains possible est que l'amour que je te porte grossit mes crainctes. Ne peulx toy de precaultions et pardessus tout mes darenieres remonstrnces..."13 /
8r La bonne dame ne peult pour le moment en dyre d'advantaige, tant estoit ja amoindrie par la maladie. Et Jehan respondict:

"Chiere et bonne mere, sera faict tout comme avés dict, et nonobstant que aye moy grant amitié pour ma cousine, se par male fortune venoye a descouvrir ens elle quoy que ce soyt contraire a honnesteté et bonnes moeurs, espoulzeroye plus tost la Juifve!"

"Oh, mon filz," reprint la bonne, "me rejecte bien loing telles parolles qui ne sont que maledictions a l'encontre d'une povre fille que ne toy ne moy ne cognoissons aulcunement. Bien est il vray que elle est juifve, et ce nonobstant n'en est pas moing une creature de Dieu, et a Luy seul appartient la juger. Croy moy bien, chier anfant, ne debvons mauldire personne a icelle fin que le bon Dieu nouz benisse. Dy moy, ha
8v elle oncques jecté sus toy male- / fice aulcun? Et s'elle estoit tant pernicieulze, l'auroit on ja lung temps chassee de l'endroict. Or cuyde moy que tout ce que ilz dysent d'icelle juifve peult bien n'estre que bourdes et calumnies.

"Quant est de moy, n'en peulx je rien dyre, pour ce que ne la cognoy point et ne l'ay veue tant seulement que une seulle foiz que s'est elle treuvee sus mon chemin, et passoit elle tant prez que l'ay touchiee. Neant moing ne peulx je affermer s'elle est belle ou layde, pour ce que estoit elle couverte d'ung grant mantel noir, et avoit sus le visaige ung voille trez espois, et faisoit peu clere a ceste heure. Neant moing est vray de confesser que rendoit elle ung trez fort odeur, ains ne peulx je acertainer se estoit odeur de soulfre ou tout aultre goust.

"Ains ne nouz ocupons de elle que prier Dieu de la convertir
9r   a nostre saincte / relligion."

Or Jehan, qui n'avoit dict cela que par fasson de dyre de l'endroict, ravalla ses parolles, promectant bien a sa mere suyvre en touts poincts ses bonnes remonstrances.

CE QUE C'ESTOIT QUE LA JUIFVE

Ores est bon de vouz apprendre ce que c'estoit que ceste juifve. Quellesque[s] annees en ça estoit veneu en la ville ung juif, et n'y en avoit encore que bien peu en icelluy temps. Le dict juif avoit amenié avecques soy une jeune fillette, une femme que l'on cuydoit estre sa servante, et ung serviteur morisque, et pour ce que estoit d'une race mauldicte, ne
9v   treuva a se / logier nulle part convenableme[n]t; voyre offrant bien payer ne treuva que repoulsades partout.

A la parfin parvint a achapter une vielle mazure du tout ruynee, et se logia la comme peult avecques sa sequelle moyennant des toilles que disposa pour se deffendre de la pluye.

Ains ne tarda point que n'eust faict bastir on lieu une moult belle maizon en bon bois de chastaigner, et peult on encore ce jour d'huy recognoistre la dicte maizon aulx engraveures et esculpteures dont est aornee et especialement a l'entour des fenestres. Et toutz se esmervelloient que ung ord juif eust faict bastir une tant belle maizon.

Cestuy juif issoit fort peu du logiz, et seulement pour aprouvisionner son mesnaige et tout ce que estoit de besoing, et jaçoit que payoit bien
10r   toutz ceulx a qui s'adressoit, luy vendoient en rechignant, / redoubtant que son argent ne feut monnoye du diable. Ains y en eust, nonobstant cela, voires mesme ung assez grant numbre qui n'eurent paour de entrer en sa maizon a icelle fin de luy emprunter de l'argent, car l'existimoit on trez riche.

Ains a quatre ans de sa veneue ou peu prez, on ne le veid plus issir de son logiz, dont l'on souspeçonna que debvoit luy estre party du pays ou mort; aulcuns disoient mesme avoir veu creuzer une fosse ens son courtil. Par ainsy, le morisque pourvoyoit en son lieu aulx besoings de la maizon.

Quant estoit des femmes, nul ne povoit se jacter les avoir envisaigees pour ce que demouroient elles toutz jours celees on logiz, et se par adventure issoient, estoient tant songneuzes a se couvrir de lungs mantelz et la teste de voilles que n'estoit possible veoir leur visaige; aussy 10v ne se faisoit on faulte de caqueter, / et n'y avoit que une seulle croyance partout, assavoir que la jeune fille estoit une orde sorciere,[14] et rejectoit on sus elle toutz malencontres et accidents qui advenoient on lieu—et notés que les griefs ne faisoient faulte! Quiconques la rencontroit en son chemin prenoit maladie: c'estoit sort jecté par la Juifve! Finablement, tout mal adveneu on pays luy estoit reprouchié.

D'advantaige, toutz disoient que s'elle estoit tant songneuse a celer son visaige, c'estoit que estoit espouvantable: que son nez sembloit bec de hibou, que avoit les oeuilz verds comme es chatz noirs et la peau comme vieil parchemin, et avoit es piedz et es mains lungues griffes; et par dessus tout, rendoit odeur de soulfre tant puant que sentoit on par ou avoit passé. Ains en voila assez, voyre mesme trop; oncques n'auroye je faict se tentoye conter tout ce que l'on disoit. Par ainsy quand l'on vou- / 11r loit affermer avoir grant desgoustement et repugnance a faire telle chose, souloit on dyre: "Ainceois que faire cela, espoulzeroye pleus tost la Juifve." Ains pour ceste juifve avons nouz lessé la bonne dame ens son lict ja espuisee; est temps que retournons a elle.

COMMENT LA BONNE ET EXCELLENTE MERE RENDIT SON AAME A DIEU

Le Pere Anthoine et Jehan ne delaissoient d'ung seul instant [le] lict de la paovre mere, e[t] se bendoient par toutz moyens a retenir sa vie. Le bon pere, esprové en telz evenementz, veid clerement que touschoit elle a sa fin, pourquoy envoya la servante querir ce que estoit de besoing 11v en[15] / tel pas, comme crucifix, benoistier, cierge, et tout. Cetemps-pendant, son souffle aloit en abaissant; a la parfin, jecta sus Jehan ung reguard bien doulx. En aprez leva les oeuilz au ciel et rendit son aame a Dieu. Lors Jehan, avoir baizé sa bonne mere, s'agenoille jouxte le lict; autant en feirent la bon pere et la vielle servante. Or n'est besoing vouz dyre que larmes, lame[n] tacions, et prieres ne feirent faulte a la bonne dame.

L'endemain, on feit les appretz de la triste coerimonie, cependant que Jehan ne mectoit fin a ses lamentacions. Le jour ensuyvant, les parentz (et n'en cognoissoit on d'aultres en l'endroict que Oudart et sa fille, ains les bons et leaulx amys ne faisoient faulte) accompagnarent le co[r] ps a l'ecclize. Le bon Pere Anthoine du tout meshaigne menoit le dueil, et de partout sus le chemin voyoit on les bonnes gentz s'agenoiller/
12r devant leurs portes et prier bien devostement pour le repos de l'aame de la defuncte, et maulgré tout ce dueil, l'on remarqua aiseement que les larmes de Messyre Ouda[r]t et de sa fille n'estoient que cingeries et feintize. A la parfin, l'office divin parachevé, l'on porta le corps au coemitiere[16] pour le mectre en la fosse, et quand l'on jecta la terre sus la biere, les escriz et gemissementz recommencearent avecques fureur et ne prindrent fin que aprez que ung chascun eust jecté l'eaue benoiste et estainct son cierge.

Adoncques Oudart print par le braz son nepveu et luy dict: "Vien avecques nouz, mon amy, pource que seroit a toy trop malplaizant a ceste heure restourner chez toy et ne plus veoir la ta bonne mere, et tascherons ma fille et moy autant que pourrons te conforter en cestuy estrif."

12v   Et le povre garson, du tout meshaigne, suyvit son/ oncle; ains notés bien que Messire Oudart estoit ung ruzé matoiz qui, n'ayant peu trufer la mere, cuydoit bien soy s'en rescompenser avecques le filz.

COMMENT LE MAULVAZ ONCLE ATTENTA ENGINER SON NEPVEU ET PERDIT SA POYNE.

Tout incontinent que entrarent on logiz, Jehan se lessa cheoir sus une chaire et se print a plorer de rechief cependent que Oudart aloit[17] se pourmener au courtil, attendent que la table feust dressee; et Remiette avecques une petite servant[e] acoustroit a dipner, et venoit souventes foys prez de Jehan par fasson de le accoiser. Finablement, la servante dressa la table, et chascun vint se placer.

13r   Or croyés que le chagrin / n'empescha ne le pere ne la fille de jouer des machoueres, ains n'estoit ainsy du povre Jehan, car avoit le gouzier tant estreint par le chagrin que les mourceaulx ne pouvoient descendre. Neant moing, son oncle, qui avoit ses viseez, ne faisoit faulte de l'encouraigier a boire et a mengier—et especialement a bo[i]re, cuydant l'enginer plus aiseement quand auroit la teste ung peu eschauffee par le vin. Ains perdoit bien sa poyne pour ceste heure: le bon Jehan ne songeoit gaire a boire. Neant moing avoit le cault oncle tant a cueur de attaindre son but sans targer, luy tint telles parolles:

    "Entend bien, mon amy, te voyla maintenant tout seulet, et te seroit trop malplaysant vivre ainsy. Souventes foys entre ton defunct pere et moy a esté projecté marier toy avecques ma bien amee fille. 13v   D'advantaige, ta bonne mere, avant que rendre son aame a / Dieu, en tesmoingnoit encore le dezir.[18] Or, dy moy naïfvement se ainsy te plaict."

    A quoy respondict Jehan: "Chier oncle, lessons pour le moment telz proupoz, car ne songe moy a ceste heure que prier le bon Dieu pour ma mere et la plourer. Neant moing, bien est il vray que je affecte grantement ma cousine·et que oncques ne treuverai femme plus a mon appetit. Ains n'est le temps de songer a cela."

    "Voire mais," feit Oudart, "ja ne m'est venue en pensement te marier le jour de l'enterrement de ta mere, et ne te parloy de cela que pour ung temps convenent. Ains, en attendant, debvons nouz nouz ocuper ung peu de l'advenir. Tu est toy encore jeune et partant point du tout duict es affaires, pourquoy fairois toy saigement me lesser l'administracion et goubvernement de ta chevance; par ainsy, le temps de ton mariaige 14r   adveneu, / treuverois ton reveneu grossi par mes soingz, et pourrois toy en jouir bauldement et paisiblement avecques ta cousine Remiette deveneue ta femme."

    "Chier oncle," respondict Jehan, " a vouz porte grant recognaissance pour la poyne que volés prendre; neant moing, doib je vouz dyre que ne suy moy tant rude on goubvernement de maizon que le pouvés cuyder. Ença troiz ans ay moy seul tout goubverné sans l'ayde de ma mere, et d'advantaige adjousteray que le Pere Anthoine a recogneu ma suffizance."

    Atant Oudart n'auza pour le moment respliquer, ains ne renonceoit pour autant a ses veues, car estoit luy moult aspre et tenant en ses opinions.

Le demourant du jour se passa bien tristement, et a la vespree, le
pere et la fille reconduisirent Jehan jusqu[e]s a la porte de sa maizon, ou
14v   treva le povre garçon sa bonne vielle servante / agenoillee jouxte le lict
vuide de la defuncte, toute en desolacion; et ne luy ne elle ne pouvoient
dyre mot, tant avoient eulx le cueu[r] estreinct et navré. A la parfin
alarent se mectre on lict, ains non pour dormir, comme debvés bien
penser.

COMMENT JEHAN ALA TREUVER LE PERE ANTHOINE ET PASSA LE JOUR CHEZ LUY

L'endemain, la bonne servante lessa son lict de bon matin et
appresta le desjeuner, et ala esveigler Jehan; ains le treuva ja du tout
vesteu et agenoillé devant une imaige de Madame la Vierge, pour qui sa
mere avoit grant devocion.

"Venés menger ung petit," feit elle, "car avés vouz besoing de
15r   reconfort, et par aprez irés treuver le bon Pere / Anthoine, et deviserés
avecques luy sus ce que sera de faire en telle passe."

Le povre garson ala se mectre a table et tenta de menger ung peu,
ains les mourceaulx ne pouvoient descendre. Finablement, avala ung
voirre de vin et s'achemina vers la retraicte du bon pere, et le treva qui
s'en revenoit de l'ecclize.

"Ha, te vecy bien a poinct," feit le pere, "car estoie moult dezireux
de te veoir. On, mon amy, tu viens de perdre une bien bonne mere qui te
portoit grant amour, et esto[i]t elle moult soulcieuze de ton advenir. Ains
debvons nouz nouz soubmettre a la saincte voulenté du bon Dieu et
accepter sanz nouz plaindre les poynes et tribulacions que il nouz envoye
a icelle fin de nouz esprouver et rendre dignes d'entrer ens son sainct
paradiz. Ains changeons ung peu de propos: tout ainsy que tu as demouré
15v   hier drez midi jusqu'a la vespree avecques ton oncle, / seroie moy moult
curieulx d'apprendre tout ce que luy ha peu te dyre."

Atant Jehan bien naïfvement conta tout sanz rien celer ne
obmectre. Avoir tout ouÿ et tout poisé, le bon pere, qui n'avoit l'esperit
ne moing bon que agu, veid trop bien que Oudart visoit a embler la
chevance du paovre Jehan, pourquoy delibera et arresta soy mectre sus

les trainees de Oudart, et loua grantement la preudence de Jehan et l'encouraigea a toujou[r]s faire ainsy, et luy dict:

"Ores lessons cela pour le moment, et dy moy bien naïfveme[n]t se il te poinct bien fort te marier avecques ta cousine."

"Bien est il vray," respondict Jehan, "que ma cousine est bien playsante, gente, accorte, et toute a mon appetit, et la prendroie moy voulentier, n'estoit que ma bonne mere par ava[n]t mourir a moy
16r grantement admonesté rien / concludre en tel pourchaz que n'aye bien estudié et espié s'elle ne se destourne en rien du droict chemin de vertu, et par especial rien fare que n'aye print conseille et assistance de vouz."

"Et ne te fauldray on besoing," feit le bon pere.

Or, comme le dipner estoit prest, touts deux vinrent se seoir a table, et Jehan commencea a menger un peu, et avoir rendu graces a Dieu, passarent la reste du jour a deviser, aprez quoy Jehan regaigna son logiz.

COMMENT LE PERE ANTHOINE SE BENDA A ENTRAVER LES MENEES

Avoir bien pourpensé et tout poisé, vied bien le bon pere que ja
16v estoit temps de espier et entraver les trainees de / Messire Oudart, pourquoy incita sa servante a attirer a soy sa petite niepce qui servoit de chambrillon a Remiette, car comptoit bien apprandre de icelle niepce tout ce qui se faisoit et disoit chez iceulx, pour ce que la dicte fillette[19] n'avoit ne moing bonne langue que fine aureille.

Pensa aussy le bon pere se renseigner a ung beaugear qui demouroit avecques une femme que l'on cuidoit estre sorciere, pour ce que elle gaignoit sa vie a vendre ungants et remedes et a dire la bonne adventure. Or ce baugear, que touts nommoient Le Brenou,[20] avoit charge chez La Sagotte (ainsy avoit nom la dicte sorciere) de faire messaiges, aler querir ce que estoit necessaire on mesnaige, comme eaue, bois, pain, viande, et tout, et la reste de son temps despendoit a
17r gueuzer par touts chemins et d'huis en huis; par ainsy / le treuvoit on touts dis en son chemin. Et cuidés bien que en menant tel train de vie, debvoit en sçavoir lung; d'avantaige, povoit on le faire jazer et tout tirer de luy en l'alichant avecques ung vo[i]rre de vin ou quelques pinarts.

Tout estant arreste[e], ainsi que venons de dyre, la bonne servante de Pere Anthoine issit de l'ost[el][21] a icelle fin de tirer a part sa petite niepce a l'insceu de ses maistres, et la treuva bien a poinct qui aloit querir de l'eaue on putz du quarroy, et eust le temps de luy dyre sanz estre veue ne entendeue de nully de venir sanz poinct de faulte la treuver l'endemain matin, a quoy respondict la fillette[22] que ne fairoit faulte a l'assignacion. De son cousté le Pere Anthoine comptoit bien treuver Le Brenou a l'issue de l'office a la porte de l'ecclize.

17v   Comme / estoit ja nuict clouse, s'appresta le bon pere a se mectre on lict.

COMMENT LA SERVANTE FEIT CAQUETER LA BECHOTE ET CE QUE TIRA D'ELLE

L'endemain de bon matin, Pasquete (ainsy avoit nom la petite niepce) ne feit faulte a se rendre a l'assignacion, et la tante, a icelle fin de bien la affrioler, luy bailla ung joli petit coulteau a manche d'ivoire et luy feit menger ung bon transon de fouace; et quant feut mengee la dicte fouace, s'enquesta se estoit elle bien traictee ou elle estoit.

"Oh, tante," respondict elle, "ha lung temps que dezire estre hors
18r   de ceste maizon, pour ce que le pere et la / fille que n'est rien de vouz dyre comme sont maulvaiz, et ha lung temps que voloie vouz semondre de me tirer de la!"

"Voire mais," feit tant[e] Ursule (ainsy la nommoit on), "que [as] tu a reprouchier a eulx?"[23]

"Oh," feit elle, "n'auroie oncques faict se voloie tout conter, et n'auseroie le faire paravant estre retiree de la."

"Ains," feit la tante, "n'est asseurément point moy qui vouldroi te encuser, pourquoi peulx tu parler sanz craincte aulcune."

"Oh," feit Pasquette, "se sçavoient eulx que suy veneue cean, seroye moy perdeue. L'aultre hier, le pere me ha baillé du nerf de boeuf tant seullement pour ce que avoie moy encqueté ung petit transon de temps avecques la voizine, et en porte je encor les frangeez sus les fesses, comme pouvés veoir: agardés!"

18v   "Povre anfant," dict la tante, "ne targera/ guiaire que ne t'aye tiree de ceste maizon. Ains est mestier que tu y demoures encor quelques jours a icelle fin de me conter comment se comporte Remiette, car pour cause (n'as toy besoing de sçavoir) doib moy cognoistre touts ses faicts et oeuvres. Par ainsy, espie la bien, et par aprez, viens tout me conter."

"Oh," feit Pasquette, "n'est ja besoing tant espier, et peulx moy vouz affier que ne se conduict elle comme fille honeste et comme damoiselle de son reng, tesmoing ce que elle ha faict ha au plus quinze jours—et [s'] apprenoit elle que vouz ay langué cela, seroie moy perdeue."

"Dy touts jours," feit la tante, "et ne crainds rien."

"Or doncques, comme vouz disoie (alés la juger par ses oeuvres: ascoutés!), ha approuchant quinze jours, atant que son pere et moy
19r   estions acouchés, ha faict / entrer ens sa chambre par la fenestre le garson de Claude Gaulthier. Ains le pere Oudart couchoit au dessoubs et ne dormoit point a ceste heure, pourquoy, oyant meiner du bruit au dessus, se leva tost et grimpa la montee a piedz deschaux, et rua dans la chambre. Or le gars, comme debvés bien penser, ne feut lent a saulter par la fenestre. Par ainsy, Remiette paya pour touts deux. Le nerf estoit tout a poinct accrochié a ung clou jouxte le lict. Oudart l'apoig[n]a et luy bailla une tant rude singlade que de tout le jour ne peut soy lever. Estoit meurdrie, et a chascuns coups jectoit plainctes et escris a effroyer. Acourt que se passoit ceste noise, mouroi moy de paour ens mon lict, et n'ausoie seullement ne bougier n[e] souffler. Amais est temps que je /
19v   m'en voise, car se faict ja tard, et ay je trop paour du nerf."

"Or apprend moy tant seullement se parlent eulx quelques foys de Messire Jehan," dist la tante.

"Oh, souventes foys," respondict Le Bechote, "et s'entendent entre eulx pour venir a fin de luy faire seigner ung parchemin appresté a l'advance, et est le dict parchemin dans le tirouer de la table. Ains ne peulx je dire ce que est de cela, pour ce que ne sçay moy point lire du tout; et par especial doib vouz dire aussy que le pere ne mect f[i]n a semondre sa fille de faire bonne voulte a Messire Jehan. Ains ne semble a elle peu chaloir de cela."

Atant la tante Ursule ren[v]oya sa niepce, luy promectant bien la retire[r]²⁴ soubs peu de cest[e] maulvaize maizon; et Pasquette, bien contente, dist:

20r   "Bone tante, / aquoisés vous. Seray moy touts jours en ascout[e], et incontinent que y aura quelque chose, vindray ma cruche sus l'ayguerie,²⁵ et soubs semblant d'aler au putz viendray tout vouz dire."

COMMENT, AVOIR FAICT BEVETER LE BRENOU, LE PER[E] ANTHOINE APPRINT DE LUY CHOSES MOULT CURIEULZES.

Pasquette²⁶ n'avoit faict dix enjambeez comme le bon Pere Anthoine restournoit de l'ecclize, et comme touschoit a sa porte, veid venir de loing Le Brenou, pourquoy l'attendit la. Et quant feut assez prez, le bon pere luy dist:

"Ou vas tu, Brenou, que tu soies tant hastif?"

20v   "Bien est vray, bon Pere," / respondict Le Brenou, "que n'ay le temps de m'amuzer ens chemin."

"Voire," reprint le pere, "point mesme le temps de humer une veguade?"

"Oh, ne vous gaussés de moy," feit Le Brenou, "car sçavés trop bien que le vin faict plus souvent faulte que la soif et le temp[s] pour le boire. D'advantaige, n'ay moy tant presse a ceste heure que ne puisse m'arraiter ung transon de temps."²⁷

"Et bien, entres," dist le pere.

Incontinent que feurent entrés, le Pere Anthoine feit mectre une breusse sus la table et l'emplit. Atant Le Brenou la vuida tout de hait, car n'en beuvoit le paovre homme que peu souvent de sy bon. Atant le bon pere, en remplissant le voirre, s'enquesta de luy comment estoit logié, 21r   comment nourry, et tout. Avoir vuidé le voirre, Le Brenou agu- / arda astou et dist:

"Debvés sçavoir, bon Pere, que je demoure avecques La Sagotte, pour ce que n'ay peu treuver azyle aultre part; et ne me traicte elle point trop bien. N'ay pour acoucher que ung taudi et ung peu d'estrein, tandi[s] que elle acouche sus ung bon coutil de boure. D'advantaige, ne me lesse a menger que ses reliefs, et quant rapporte moy a l'ost[el] quelques bons morceaulx que me baillent les bonnes gentz (comme trenche de jambon, de pasté, viande, pain, fruicts, et tout), prend pour soy le meilleur et me lesse le pire. Oultre plus, quant suy moy endormi, vient elle tout doulcettement a piedz deschaux et tire de ma pouche les angelots que ay amassés on porche de l'ecclize ou par les chemins."

21v   "Amais," reprint le Pere Anthoine, "pourquoy / demoures tu avecques elle?"

"Vouz l'ay ja dict," respondict Le Brenou, "pour ce que nuz ne veult me logier. Neant moing debvroit elle mieulx me traicter, pour ce que n'ha aultre que moy pour faire ses messaiges, aler querir eaue, vin, pain, bois, et tout; et ha lung temps que avoie faim de tout dyre, ains ne l'ay je faict, craincte que elle ne me baillat le bouquon."

"Et que auroi[es] tu dict?" feit le pere, en versant a boire. Avoir vuidé le goubelet, Le Brenou agarda astou, et quant feut acertainé que nuz n'estoit en ascout[e], dist:

"Oh, Pere Anthoine, estes cogneu partout pour ung bien sainct homme, pour quoy ay plaine fiance en vouz, et n'ay craincte aulcune que me encusiez; par ainsy, vay tout vouz conter.

22r   "Ha approuchant unze ans, Magdelon / Gobreau, cogneue ce jour d'huy seullement soubs le nom de Sagotte, demouroit ens une logette que povés veoir encor jouxte le barri[28] du jard, et moy ens une aultre, de fasson que noz logiz de elle et de moy n'estoient partiz que par ung petit courtil. Or ceste fille trevoit bien meilleur laborer du cropion que des doigtz: meinoit vie de vraye pute, et recepvoit a l'anuitan[29] tantost l'ung tantost l'aultre, si bien que ung beau jour se treuva affins preigne. Et feit tant par fasson de se vestir que treuva moyen de celer l'enlevure de son ventre, ains ne peult tant fare que peult me decepvoir; ains ne feis semblant de rien sçavoir. Or ung jour que ne dormoy point, encore que feut bien avant dedans la nuict, entendi elle se douloir et poulser des / 22v plainctes. Or me doubtai de l'affaire; tout soubdain, alai [me] mectre en ascout[e], et regarday par une fente. Oh, bon Pere! Ne sçai se ause dire la reste!"

"Dy touts jours," feit le bon pere, "et conte sus ma preudance."

"Or, que la voulenté de Dieu et la vostre soyent faictes," feit Le Brenou. "Or veid que elle estoit assize a terre, et avoit devant elle ung anfant nouveau nay. Atant me ruay ens la chambre a icelle fin de prester assistance on besoing. Et me hastai de ramasser l'anfant et le mectre sus le lict; ains le paovre innocent estoit mort estranglé, et avoit encore le lasset a son col. Atant reculay moy d'espouvente et la traictai comme meritoit elle, et me deliberoie de aler declarer tel caz au prevost quant me retint elle et me dist: /

23r   " 'Ascoutes bien, Pierre' (en cestuy temps ne m'appeloit on encore Le Brenou), 'se tu as le maltàlent de bougier de ceans par avant de avoir aydé moy a anfoïr cest anfant, et se oncques te prenoit envie de lascher tant seullement ung mot de cela, affieroie moy que tu en es le pere et que c'est toy qui l'as estranglé maulgré et envi mes prieres. Par ainsy, se tout venoit en apert, la chorde ne te fairoit faulte comme a moy.'

"En tel estrif, ne sçavoie moy quoy deliberer. Finablement, me resignay a faire tout comme voloit elle; pourquoy alai creuzer ung trou ens ung coing du courtil, tandi[s] que la maulvaize fille mectoit l'anfant ens ung viel pot de terre, le ployant en deux pour le faire entrer, en le

23v foullant aussy / avecques son pied. Et quant feut le pot dedans le trou, a icelle fin de ne faire sou[p]ceonner que l'on avoit remué la terre pour ensepulturer la ung anfant, ay planté sus le pot ung jeune couldre, et du depuis ha tant creu le dict couldre que est deveneu ung grant arbre, comme pourrez (se vouz en prend envie) le veoir anui, tout chargié de noizilles."

"Trez bien," dist le bon Pere Anthoine, "te rend graace de me avoir conté tout cela, et m'en serviray on besoing; pour tant ne crainds aulcunement que [mal] t'en advienne.[30] Humettes encore une veguade, et prends cest escut; atant fay ton messaige."

"Oh," feit Le Brenou, "auray tost faict: ne s'agit que de tirer a part la damoiselle Remiette et de luy dire venir a la vespree chez La Sagotte." /

24r   "Voire mais," feit le pere, "Remiette va doncques quelques foys chez La Sagotte?"

"Oh, souventes foys," feit Le Brenou, "ains touts jours anui,[31] craincte d'estre veue."

"Ha, ha!" pourpensa le bon pere a par soy, "ay maintenant de quoy ent[r]aver les trainees de Messire Oudart." Atant renvoya Le Brenou, en luy recommandant par especial de garder bien secretement tout ce que venoient de dyre.

COMENT LE PERE ANTHOINE SOUBMIT LA SAGOTTE, ET CE QUE EXIGEA DE ELLE

Jusques la, le bon pere n'avoit perdeu son temps ne sa poyne, et ne 24v luy restoit plus que assubj[e]ctir La / Sagotte a sa voulenté—et avoit de quoy faire cela. Par ainsy, l'envoya tost cercher par sa servante; or incontinent que feut veneue, le bon pere la feit passer ens une chambre a part, et luy dist:

"Ascoute bien, Magdelon, t'ay faict venir ceans a ceste fin d'avoir renseignement de toy sus ung caz moult esmerveillable. On dist que aulcunes foys on veoid ung esperit on courtil de la logette que tu as habitee ha unze ans ou peu prez. Or, acourt le temps que tu as demouré la, auroies tu veu toy quelque chose de semblable?"

A ce La Sagotte veid bien que cela ne presagioit rien de bon; neant moing s'appresta a payer de oultrecuidance, et respondict:

"Oncques n'ay rien veu, Reverend Pere, qui assemble a cela, et 25r cuyde / moy que iceulx qui disent cela ne sont que mocqueurs et conteurs de bourdes."

"Ha, tu penses cela? Neantmoing," reprint le pere, "si esse que ung bien preudhomme qui merite toute fiance m'ha asseré que passant par la a l'anuitan ha veu dans le feuillaige du couldre qui est on coing du courtil l'aame d'ung tout petit anfant nouveau nay, et avoit le dict anfant le col estranglé avecque ung lasset, et de sa petite voix crioit: 'Baptesme! Baptesme!' "

Toute incontinent, La Sagotte se feit rouge comme escrevisse cuicte, et s'apresta a payer d'oultrecuidance.

"Or ay pensé que seroit bon, pour aquoiser ceste aame en poyne, de aler la conjurer de ne plus revenir et arrachier le couldre en telle fasson qu'il n'en reste en terre la moindre racine et, / paravant de remplir le trou, y mectre ung pot d'eaue benoite, puis aprez dire prieres et oraizons a ce requises."

25 v

De rouge que elle estoit, La Sagotte devint paale comme suaire, car veid trop bien que son crime estoit cogneu et que ne luy prouficteroit rien de nier, pourquoy se jecta a genoilz es piedz du Pere Anthoine, requerant mercy. Le bon pere la releva et dict:

"Or, tu veoids que ta vie est ens mon pouvoir; neant moing, maulgré la grandeur de ta coulpe, veulx bien moy te prendre a mercy, ains par tel pacte que tu seras du tout devouee a moy et sanz poinct de faulte tu obeiras aveuglemen[t] a toutes mes voulentz."[32]

Or debvés bien penser [que] ceste mere cruelle n'avoit que a se soubmettre a tout. Affia au bon pere / que meshuy se mectoit ens sa subjec[t]ion sanz reserve aulcune, et promit d'obeir sanz poinct de faulte a toutz ordres venant de luy. Adoncques le Pere Anthoine luy dist:

26 r

"Sçai moy que la fille de Oudart va souvent chez toy. Or ay moy besoing de bien cognoistre tout son train de vie, et par especial comment elle et son pere en usent avecques Jehan. Par ainsy, estudies la bien, de fasson que ne puisse elle se doubter de rien, aprez quoy tu viendras tout me conter. D'advantaige, veulx que tu fasses avecques elle tout ainsy que souloies le faire paravant nouz estre entendeus. Par ainsy, s'elle requiert de toy receptes ou predictions de l'advenir—voire mesme bru[v] aiges a jecter sortz et malefices—contentes la et viens tost tout / me conter songnesement. Atant pourray moy empeschier le mal on besoing."

26 v

"Sera faict, tout comme avés commandé," respondict La Sagotte. "Ains est temps que je m'en voise, pource que Remiette doibt estre a ceste heure chez moy."

"Eh bien, va," dist le pere, "et recordes toy bien que tu seras rescompensee selon tes oeuvres!"

COMMENT LE PERE ANTHOINE LESSA ALER LES CHOSES A CELLE FIN DE MIEULX CONFONDRE OUDART ET SA FILLE

Cependent que les choses aloient ainsy, Jehan, comme de coustume, veoyoit sa cousine toutz les jours; et tant plus la frequentoit, tant plus l'agreant- / oit, et la treuvoit a son appetit. Les saiges admonestations de sa bonne mere ja commenceoient a s'affaiblir dans son esperit, et se complaisoit a penser que, toute preudente et prouveoyante que estoit sa mere, avoit elle bien peu juger trop rigoureusement Oudart et sa fille, d'autant plus que n'avoit elle revelé ses crainctes que par fasson de doubte.

27r

Cependent, le Pere Anthoine ne s'endormoit point, et sanz faire semblant aulcun, suyvoit diligentement Jehan pas a pas en toutes ses desmarches et actions; neantmoing, ne luy disoit mot a le destourner de sa cousine, pour ce que valoit bien mieulx que s'en degousta soy mesme; par ainsy, aloit assiez souvent le veoir, ne luy conseillant rien ou peu de chose, l'admonestant seullement de oncques / seigner parchemins[33] aulcuns se son oncle requeroit cela de luy.

27v

Les choses se passarent ainsy ung mois ou peu prez, acourt lequel temps le Pere Anthoine amassoit de toutes parts, et en avoit ja prou pour mectre empeschement au mariaige de Jehan. Ains est temps que restournons a Oudart et a sa fille et veoir ce que font chez eulx.

COMMENT OUDART ET SA FILLE VOULURENT ENGINER JEHAN

Avoir[34] bien pourpensé et grabelé, Oudart existima que tant plus targeroit, tant plus auroit de poyne a venir a ses fins; appela sa fille et luy tint / telz propos:

28r

"Tu scés, ma fille, combien ay d'amour pour toy. Oncques ne t'ay lessee avoir faulte de rien; tout ce que tu as peu desirer, te l'ay achapté, comme beaulx accoutrements, belles cottes, gorgias, coueffes, houzeaux mignons, aguillettes,[35] armilles, anneaux d'aureielles, agraphes acoustrees de jayet, ceintures aurees, corps busqué[s],[36] bagues, et tout."

"Voire," dist Remiette, "n'avés vous rien obmis?"

"Et quoy?" feit le pere.

"Et ce beau nerf de boeuf," reprint elle, "avecques quoy n'y ha point lung temps m'avés flanqué une tant rude singlade que huict jours en aprez auroit on peu compter les frangeez sus mes fess[e]s!"

"Endaz," feit le pere, "ne te complainds de cela, pour ce que
28v l'avoies toy trop bien / merité: poise tu rien avoir a l'anuitan introduict ung jeune gars en ta chambre?"

"Ne l'ay point introduict," respliqua Remiette, "car c'est maulgré et envi ma voulenté que est entré par la fenestre que Pasquette avoit obmis de clore; et ne veoys moy grant mal a cela, veu que me l'avés lessé frequenter pieça lung temps et que doib me marier a luy."

"Tu scés bien," reprint Oudart, "que le pere ne veult assentir a ce mariaige, pour ce que ne peulx je te bailler dost a sa convenance."

"Oh," feit elle, "ne me chault de cela! Sçauray bien par tel engin affoler le filz de moy a tel poinct que contraindra bien son pere a assentir."

"Voire," dist le pere, "de quel engin veulx tu parler?" "C'est,"
29r respondict elle, "une mistion dont La Sagotte / ha baillé a moy la recepte, et icelluy a qui en auray faict boire tant seullement ung traict que soubdain sera enamouré de moy a tel poinct que sera luy contraint de faire tout ce que commandaray sanz que puisse s'en deffendre en aulcunes fassons."

"Par ainsy," feit le pere, "en en faisant boire Jehan, tu pourroies l'affoler de toy a tel poinct?"

"N'y ha doubte!" dict elle, "car La Sagotte est moult esprouvee es practiques de sorcelleries. Ains n'ay que faire de l'affoler de moy, pour ce que ne veulx aulcunement me marier a luy. Ores veoid je bien que n'estoit point pour rien que me rappeliez voz largesses!"

"Et bien," dict le pere, "ne te parleray plus de l'espoulzer.[37] Ameine le seulement a seigner le parchemin qui doibt me rendre /

29v maistre d'une bonne part de sa chevance; par ainsy pourray bailler a toy
bonne dost, et n'est doubte aulcun que le pere Gaulter ne soit content de
t'avoir pour bru."

"Pere," feit Remiette, "pour ce qui est de cela, pouvés compter sus
moy!"

"Par ainsy," reprint le pere, "a celle fin de le bien allicher et le
prendre comme oizel a la glue et poisson a l'haim, tu va te bien affierer et
atorner; par aprez, tu iras le convier a souper demain chez nouz. Atant tu
te mecteras a table a costé de luy, et auras soing de le bien affrioler et par
especial le bien inciter a boire. Lors, sus le tard, soubs semblant d'aler me
refreschir on courtil, te lesseray seulle avecques luy. Ains iray me
30r musser ens la chambre a / costé, dond pourray tout entendre. Mes que ne
seray plus la, tu l'amorseras par belles parolles, mignardizes, petits
baizers, pigeonneries, blandissements, et tout. Puis luy fairas boire ton
bruvaige magique, et pour en finer, luy fairas seigner le parchemin, qui
sera on tirouer de la table. Aprez quoy rentreray, et soubs pretext[e] que
se faict tard, l'envoyeons acouchier."

"Pere," dist Remiette, "faray moy tout comme avés dict, et
apporteray a ce que dezirés tout bon vouloir. Neant moing, cela ne peult
estre faict paravant troys ou quatre jours, pour ce que pour aprester le
bruvaig[e] ay besoing d'estre en male sepmaine."

"Et bien, attendons," dist le pere.

30v Or notés que Pasquette, l'aureille a la fente, n'avoit / perdeu mot de
ce que avoit esté dict. Aussy, soubs semblant de aler a l'eaue, print elle
tost sa cruche et ala tout languer a sa tante.

COMENT LE TEMPS SE PASSA ATANT QUE REMIETTE
EUST SES FLEUR[S]

Comme avons dict, La Bechotte ala tout conter a sa tante, qui
incontinent le rechanta au Pere Anthoine. Adoncques le bon pere veid
trop bien que estoit temps d'en finer avecques Oudart et sa fille,
pourquoy pour plus d'enseignements songeoit a envoyer cercher La

Sagotte. Ainz n'en eust point la poyne, car mecto[i]t elle le pied sus /
31r l'esseuil, et quant feut entree, le bon pere luy dist:

"M'est adviz que tu en as prou a nouz conter."

"Oh," feit elle, "apporte a vouz telles nouvelles que en serés tout
estommi! Ascoutés: depuis ung mois encea, Remiette me pourchasse a
icelle fin d'avoir moyen de enamourer d'elle ung jeune gars que convoite
elle en mariaige; et est encore venue arsoir pour cela, ains pour en assaier
avecques son cousin Jehan. Or, comme m'avés commandé de tout faire a
son bandon, luy ay apprins a composer tel bruvaige d'amour que, quant
en aura elle faict boire tant seullement ung traict a icelluy que vouldra
envouster, sera tout incontinent maitresse de luy a tel poinct que le faira
elle obeir a son plaizir sanz que luy puisse s'en deffendre."

31v   "Et quel / bruvaige est ce?" feit le pere.

"Ascoutés bien," feit elle, "va[y] [38] moy vouz le dyre. Doibt elle
prendre a ung cierge qui aura esté allumé a la veiglee d'une jeune pucelle
morte ung transon de cire gros comme ung oeuf de coulon; puis la
mectera soubs son aiscelle senestre; et quant sera bien ramollie la dicte
cire, la maniera bien ens ses doigz avecques troiz de ses chevueilz, troiz
poilz de son aiscelle senestre, et troiz poilz de son amary, et l'estendra et
arrondira a la fasson d'ung petit torteau. Puis, a tout son affiche a
chevueilz, trassera a chascuns coings d'ung quaré quatre lectres en tel
ordre que s'ensuit: [. . .] [39] atant, on coing senestre d'en hault le lectre '*R*,'
32r premiere de son nom de baptesme, et aulx / deux aultres coing[s] du
quarré trassera en tel ordre les lectres des noms de icelluy que vouldra
elle envouster, aprez quoy trassera ung cueur danz le quarré, et plantera
son affiche on mitan du dict cueur. Atant mectra le tout danz une escuelle
neufve; par aprez attachera a son amary une petite esponge masle, et
quant sera bien inbué du sang de ses fleurs, la dicte esponge l'espreindra
sus le torteau. Et tost aprez, remplira l'escuelle de bon hypocras, et
lessera destremper le tout acourt une heure. Atant mectra l'hypocras ens
une guedoufle bien estoupee, en atte[n]dant le mome[n]t d'en user."

"Amaz," feit le Pere Anthoine, "cecy est vray raǵoust d'enfer, et ja
ne te prendray pour cuisiniere!"

32v   "Oh, Reverend / Pere!" reprint La Sagotte, "ne vouz mocqués!
Ceste mistion est d'effaict asseuré. Ores doib je aussy vouz dire que

Remiette doibt meshui semondre on lendemain Jehan. Ainz est temps que je m'en voise; se d'huy a demain y ha du nouveau, viendray tost a vouz."

"Et bien, vas t'en," dist le bon pere.

COMMENT REMIETTE ALA SEMONDRE JEHAN A SOUPER

Tout ainsy que La Sagotte l'avoit dict [au] Pere Anthoine, s'estre bien affieree, atouree, testonnee, aornee, et tout, Remiette ala treuver son cousin, et ne pouvoit on refuser que ainsy acoustree ne feut elle
33r moult / alichante. Et tout en entrant commencea a le tanser ainsy:

"Vere, gentil cousin, cuidons nouz que vouz nouz avés mis a part, car y ha tantost huict jours que n'avés mis le pied sus nostre esseuil. Veoyons, auriez vouz aiques a nouz reprouchier?"

"Oh, nenny!" feit Jehan, "n'ay peu aler vouz veoir pource que avoie moy grant besongne. Tenés, agardés toutz ces parchemins que avoye a grabeler, et se le Pere Anthoine ne m'estoit veneu en ayde, n'auroye je peu encore achever telle besongne."

"Voire mais," feit elle, "auriés vouz esté mieulx advizé requerant ayde de vostre oncle, qui ha plus grant estudie de vouz que cestuy cagout, dont ne peulx moy me deffendre de me meffier? D'advantaige, aulcunz /
33v asserent avoie veu luy souventes foys entrer a l'anuitan chez la Juifve. En toutz cas, croyés bien que n'est luy aussy grant sainct que veult le paroistre! Ores, veoid je bien que a ceste heure, n'avés plus fiance en nouz, et ce m'est d'autant plus m[a]lplayzant que moy vouz ay toutz jours aymé bien tenellement."

"Et moy, belle cousine, ne vouz ayme je point tout autant?"

"Alons, alons," feit elle, "asserés le par ung bon baizer, et que tout soyt dict."

Atant Jehan la baiza avecques modesteté et reverence sus les deux joues.

"Oh, oh!" dist Remiette, "se ne m'aimés que comme sçavés baizer, beau cousin, peulx je moy affermer que vouz ne m'aimés guiaire. Tenés!"

34r   Et tout incontinent luy jecta les / bras au col et apliqua ses lebvres moites sus sa bouche, en la quelle fourra sa langue grillante et endemenee av[e]cques telle paillardize que le naïf Jehan en feut remué jusques au tresfund de sa fressure. Atant tout ravi d'ayse, estreignit voluptueusement sa cousine sus son sein, en se pasmant de joie.

Lors la ruzee pute, jugeant que y en avoit assiez pour le moment, se despestra de l'estreinte et dist:

"Voire mais, estoie venue vouz con[v]ier a souper demain chez nouz; et debvons nouz compter sus vouz?"

"Oh, belle cousine! Comptés sus moy sanz poinct de faulte!"

"Adoncques vay vouz lesser," reprint elle, "pour ce que mon pere m'attend, et n'est luy point endurant."

34v   "Oh," dist Jehan, / "ne vouz partirés de moy que ne m'ayez baillé encore ung baizer comme icelluy que venés de me bailler!"

"Oh, point!" feit Remiette, en soubriant, "attendrés a demain, car telz baizers ne se prodiguent point. Tenés, en attendant, baizés ma main."

Jehan se saisit de ceste mignone petite main logiee bien a l'estroict ens ung guant de peau trez deliee et bien doulce a l'attouchement; et rendoit le dict guant odeur plus souef que ambre et zivette. Aussy se print il a manier et baizer ameusément ceste main partout—sus le dos, sus les doigtz, et especialement danz le creux—et ne se pressoit point de lascher.

"Ores," dist Remiette, "lessés moy m'en aler! Vouz ay ja dict que mon pere n'est point endurant, et ne me chault de taster du nerf de 35r   boeuf en / rentrant on logiz!"

"Oh!" feit Jehan, "c'est que vostre main est sy doulce et ce guant sent sy bon!"

"Et bien," feit elle, "gardés le en recordacion de moy, et me le rendrés demain."

Jehan tira le guant, ains ne lascha la main que ne l'eust bien baizee toute nue sus le dos et danz le creux.

Atant Remiette s'eschappa et ala tost tout conter a son pere, a ce que Pasquette estoit en ascout[e], et ne feit faulte la mesquine d'aler incontinent tout languer a sa tante, et la tante au Pere Anthoine.

COMMENT JEHAN VEID SA MERE EN SONGE ET EN FEUT MOULT EFFROYÉ

Jehan tresque a icelluy jour n'avoit aymé sa cousine que comme soeur et amie d'anfance, ains / le baizer que elle luy avoit baillé avoit esveiglé en luy ung sentiment tout nouveau et encore incogneu de luy. Par ainsy ne duroit plus ens sa peau, tant estoit poinct de bruslants dezirs; aussy ne pouvoit luy se saouler de manier, flairer, et baizer le guant que luy avoit lessé elle.

35v

D'aultre part, estoit moult angoissé et fasché de ce que avoit dict Remiette du bon pere. Et tant plus pourpensoit, tant plus s'esgaroit ens ses pensements; car d'une part, n'ausoit luy soubceonner de calumnie sa cousin[e], dont estoit tant affolé, d'aultre part, ne pouvoit luy sans ingratitude subspecter le bon Pere Anthoine, que luy avoit esté tant secourable et devost en toutz poincts. Par ainsy, estoit en / grant fascherie et soucy et tout ambigu de ce que debvoit croyre, pourquoy la reste du jour luy sembla bien longue.

36r

F[i]nablement, sa bonne servante l'appela pour souper, ainz estoit luy trop stimulé et esguillonné de poignants dezirs que songeat luy a menger. Et quant feut temps de aler s'acouchier, ne pouvoit guiaire esperer sommeil, tant la seulle remenbrance du baizer de Remiette luy fouettoit le sang—et n'avoit luy pour toute solacion que le guant a baizer (aussy ne s'en faisoit il faulte!). Neant moing, se demena tant ens son lict, tant sus le costé dextre que sus le senestre et sus dos et sus ventre, que fina par clore les paupieres; ains ce feut pour resver.

36v   Or, songeoit que estreignoit / Remiette et tentoit luy planter ung baizer sus la bouche; ains tant plus ses lebvres aprouchoient, tant plus celles de Remiette s'eslongnoient, et on moment ou cuydoit le[s] ataindre, glissa elle de ses bras et ala prendre ens une armare une jolie coupe cristalline plaine d'hypocraz que elle luy pr[e]senta. Jehan la print, et ja la portoit a ses lebvres quand, on lieu de Remiette, veid sa mere avecques visaige severe qui luy dist:

    "As tu doncques mis en oubliance les admonestations que t'ay faictes a mon lict de mort?"

    Et, avoir dict, arracha la coupe de la main de Jehan et la jecta rudement a terre, dont se rompit en mille esclats avecques tel bruit que
37r Jehan en sursaulta sus son lict et s'esveigla, moult effroyé et tout en / sueur.

    Le jour commenceoit a aparoir. Jehan se vestit et, tout esmeu de son songe, ala tout droict a la tombe de sa mere; et feut bien estommi de la treuver toute jonchee de fleurs, et y en avoit de tant belles que, a les veoir, estoit apert que n'avoient elles poussé on lieu, et debvoient venir de payz estrange. Atant Jehan s'engenoilla et, avoir bien prié, s'avoya chez le bon pere.

COMMENT LE PERE ANTHOINE REVELA TOUT A JEHAN

    Comme Jehan mectoit le pied sus l'esseuil, treuva la bien a poinct le bon pere, qui s'en revenoit de l'ecclize et qui luy dist de prime face:

37v   "Oh, / mon povre garson! Ton viaire soucieux et chagrin ne me dist rien de bon. Veoyons, contes moy cela, se pourtant tu as encore quelleque fiance en moy (car pourroie je en doubter d'aprez ce que ta cousine ha dict de moy)."

    "Voire mais," feit Jehan, "qui ha peu vouz dyre cela?"

    "Oh," feit le pere, "en scés moy bien d'aultres, comme tu vas le veoir tanttost. Ains lessons cela pour le moment, et contes moy ton cas."

    Lors Jehan conta son songe, et tout ambigu de ce que debvoit en penser, en requerroit interpretacion.

"Oh," feit le Pere Anthoine, "cecy n'est point jeu vain d'imagin-
acion, mais bien advertissement d'en hault, et cela est sy vray que la
38r coupe que Remiette te presentoit en songe / te la presentera elle enhuy a la
desserte du souper. Ains est temps de tout mectre en apert, et te dy moy
de prime face que tu ne doibs plus penser a ceste tant maulvaize fille. Or
escoutes."

Atant le bon pere revela tout a trac a Jehan: toutes les trainees,
meinees, et engins que Oudart et sa fille machinoient a l'encontre de
luy—et par especial le train de vie de Remiette avecques son amoureux
et tout, sanz celer ne obmettre les moindres incidents.

A ce Jehan demoura ung moment sanz rien dyre, tant estoit
pantois, estommi, et aheuri; et n'estoit le Pere Anthoine qui eust tout mis
en apert, oncques n'auroit peu croyre a telle maulvaisetié de sa cousine.
38v Affins Jehan, comme / venant de faire ung songe, tout soubdain se jecta
danz les braz du bon pere, ne treuvant parolles capables pour tesmoingner
sa recognoissance. A ce le bon pere l'estreignoit amiablement et le
re[c]onfortoit de son mieulx, promectant luy treuver femme douce,
bonne, vertueze, et par especial bien plus belle que sa cousine.

"Oh, bon Pere," dist Jehan, "peulx je vouz asseurer par l'imaige de
Madame la Vierge, en laquelle ma bonne mere avoit grant devocion, que
ne remectray les piedz chez eulx; oultre plus espoulzeroie plus tost la
Juifve!"

"Lesse ceste Juifve," reprint le Pere Anthoine, "qui n'en peult
mais des chiffrements et engins de ta male cousine, que tu doibs
respudier a tout jamais. Neant moing, tu iras encore a ce soir
39r souper / avecques elle, a ceste fin de la confondre. Par ainsy, de prime
entree, tu contrefairas comme se toy ne sçavois rien, et quant a la fin du
souper aura mis elle ens ton voïrre le poison magique, en ung mot tu luy
diras son faict tout a plat; et tout incontinent pour esviter noise
av[e]cques ton oncle tu prendras la fuitte.

COMMENT JEHAN ALA SOUPER CHEZ SON ONCLE, ET CE QUI S'ENSUYVIT

N'eust esté la craincte de desplayre au bon pere, Jehan se seroit
bien passé d'aler souper chez son oncle; ainz avoit trop bien promis pour

39v   y faire faulte. Or maulgré son / eslongnement a faire cela, s'apresta a y aler; pourtant ne se hasta point trop, car entra que la table estoit ja accoustré.

     Remiette l'accuellit bien gratieusement et luy tendit la main que Jehan print, mais sanz la baizer, et luy rendit son guant. Et a ce qu'elle aloit cercher les viandes ens la cuysine, Jehan s'assit sus une chaire jouxte la table. Et come estoit prez du tiroer, s'advisa luy de le tirer, et veid le parchemin tout prest, atout le cornet et la canne a escripre. Ainz le repoulsa tost, car en avoit assiez veu.

     Lors Remiette et Pasquette aportarent les viandes, tandi[s] que le pere entroit, et se mirent toutz a table. Jehan mengea trez peu et beut

40r   encore moing, maulgré / les instances et incitementz de son oncle et de sa cousine. Et quant la desserte feut prouche de finer, Oudart lessa la table soubz semblant d'aler se pou[r]mener on courtil, comme sçavons que estoit conveneu par advance.

     Lors Remiette commencea a mectre en jeu toutz moyens d'enveloper Jehan ens ses laqz, comme belles parolles, mignardizes, pigeonneries, blandissements, et tout; ainz ne chaloit plus a Jehan de tout cela, pourquoy demouroit coy et tranquile. Atant veid bien elle que perdoit sa poyne et que ja estoit temps de luy bailler le poison d'amour. Luy dist:

     "Vere, beau cousin, n'estes vouz guiaire gaillard a ce soir, et

40v   semblés prins de soucy ou chagrin; or sçauray bien / moy vouz remectre en gayté avecques ung peu de bon hypocraz."

     Adoncques se leva et ala tirer d'une armaire une petite guedoufle, pu[i]s se rassit a costé de Jehan, et avoir empli son voirre, dist en le luy presentant:

     "Tenés, mon coulon, cecy dechassera toutes melancholies hors de vostre esperit, et vouz rameinera en gayté, et quant aurés beu, bailleray moy ung bon baizer comme sçavés."

     Or le moment d'en finer estant veneu, Jehan se leva et luy dist tout a plat:

     Aprenés, belle cousine, que ne veulx ne de vostre baiser ne de cestuy desgoustant bruvaige, avecques quoy cuydés m'envouster a icelle fin de me faire seigner le parchemin qui est ens icelluy tirouer!"

41r   A poyne avoit dict que se n'eust reculé d'ung / pas, Remiette, tout paale de cholere, luy eust arrachié les oeuilz.

"Vas, maulvaiz," dist elle, "sçauray bien me revenger, et fairay tant que ne puisses toy trouver aultre femme que la Juifve!"

Et incontinent dist a son pere, qui entroit: "Attendés, Pere, va[y] vouz cerche[r] le nerf de boeuf, et le luy flanquerés tant et tant astou du corps que ne puisse plus se tenir sus ses jambe[s], et en aprez le jecterons nouz hors de ceans!"

Pasquette, qui estoit en ascout[e] ens la cuysine, dressa les aureilles entendant parler du nerf, car en tel estrif redoubtoit d'en avoir sa part, pource que debvoit elle estre soubceonnee d'avoir langué; pourquoy saulta tost sus l'huis; et sanz soucy de le reclore s'ensaulva a belles 41v jambes se resfugier / chez sa tante.

Tout soubdain, Jehan prouficta de l'ouverture et s'enfuit de son costé; ainz par meschoir, avoir bien courreu, cuydant avoir eschappé a son oncle, feit ung glissement, s'estendist tout de son long, et sa teste choppa contre une piere, dont s'esvanouit.

Oudart le suyvoit de prez, et tout furieux, ja levoit le braz pour le congner, quant par fortune pour Jehan que le bon Dieu voleut que feust la ung home qui luy apoigna le[40] braz et luy tira le nerf de la main. Mais pour autant ne le lessa aler que ne luy eust flanqué le nerf astou du corps tant et tant de foyz du col aulx talons[41] et des talons au col que le paovre 42r Oudart ne peust que a grant poyne regaigner son logiz. / Ainz tant navré, meurdri, et meshaigne que povoit estre, ne debvons nouz le plaindre, car en avoit luy merité bien d'advantaige.

COMMENT JEHAN REVINT A LUY GISANT SUS UNG BON LICT ET FEUT SONGNÉ PAR UNE JEUNE ET GENTE PUCELLE

Quant Jehan reprint ses esperitz, feut bien estommi de se treuver acouchié sus ung bon lict on lieu d'estre estendeu par terre. Et la chambre estoit sy riche et sy belle que de sa vie n'avoit luy veu rien qui peust approuchier de cela; toutz les mebles, comme table, armare, dressouer,

42v   bahut, chaires, et tout, / estoi[en]t⁴² de bois indicques ou aultres payz
      estranges, et estoient les dicts meubles si artificieusement esculptés,
      engravés, et encroustés d'yvoire et d'argent que c'estoit a esjouir la veue.

      Mais tout cela n'estoit rien au regua[r]d d'une jeune fille qui
      acoustroit medicament a la blessure que s'estoit faicte en cheant; et estoit
      sy belle la dicte fille que n'eust esté avoir desfaulte de reverence envers
      Madame la Saincte Vierge auroit on peu dyre que elle la oultrepassoit en
      beaulté. Pourtant, en ce moment estoit elle despourveue de toutz atours,
      et n'avoit aultre vestement que une robe longue de toille trez deliee
43r   ramassee sus ses reins par une ceinture de cuir de Marocque, / garnie
      d'une boucle d'or richement acoustree de pierres pretieuses.

      Or debvés bien penser que Jehan feut moult abaubi par tant de
      beaultez! Aussy agardoit partout, pensant que cela pouvoit bien n'estre
      que ung songe. Atant la belle fille luy dist:

      "Comment estes vouz maintenant? Et n'avés vouz besoing de
      aiques? Dytes, Messire Coquault, tout ce qui est ceans est a vost[r]e
      bandon."

      A quoy Jehan respondict: "Oh, belle damoiselle, ou plustost ange
      du ciel (car ne peulx je croire que estes de ce munde, mais bien ung ange
      du pardiz qui m'est veneu en ayde en mon meschoir), or dytes moy ou suy
      en ce moment et quelle vouz estes ou se tout cecy n'est point ung songe!"

43v   "Messire Jehan," / reprint la belle fille, "ne suy moy point ung
      ange, comme venés de dyre, ainz une povre fille qui ha eu l'heur de vouz
      venir en ayde on besoing; et pour tout loyer que vouz ay faict, requierre
      tant seullement de vouz de ne point me contraindre a vouz dyre quelle je
      suy. Possible est que le sçaurés ung jour; en attendent, ne songés qu'a
      vouz guarir. Vostre playe n'est point maulvaize, et l'ay acoustree
      avecques tel baulm que ne targera point a se reprendre. Cependent, vay
      vouz bailler ung peu de bon vin, a celle fin de vouz reconforter."

      Avo[i]r dict, la belle fille print sus le dressouer une belle c[o]upe
      cristalline, puis l'emplit et la luy presenta. Or, comme Jehan agardoit
44r   tout hebeté, "Craignés / vouz," dist elle, "que ce soit poison? Veez!" Et
      elle en beut ung bon traict. Atant Jehan print la coupe et beut dehait,
      mectant ses lebvres ou la belle fille avoit mis les siennes—et de sa vie
      n'avoit gousté vin qui aprouchat de celluy la!⁴³

Atant la belle fille luy dist: "Se volés haster vostre guarison, est mestier que faciez ung bon somme." Et s'en ala, lessant toutes foys ung chandelier garni de chandelles de cire allumees.

Lors que Jehan feut seul, ne pouvoit se saouler contempler songneusement toutz les beaulx meubles et par especial le lict sus [lequel] gisoit, car esto[i]t sy beau le dict lict que c'estoit merveille. Le poele, richement festonné et aorné de houpes d'or, estoit sousteneu par 44v quatre / columnes de bois d'ebene artificieusement esculptees et engravees simulant naïfvement feuillaiges, fleurs, fruictz, oyselz, et tout; et les courtines de beau drap de soye estoient bigarees et frengees d'or, et la reste a l'advenant—en brief, pouvoit on asserer que rien n'estoit sy beau.

Or, quant eust le bon Jehan pourmené ses regards tout astou, veid jouxte [le] lict une chaire sus la quelle y avoit des acessements de femme. Or jugea bien que debvoit luy estre sus le lict de la belle fille; sy n'eust desfaulte d'en baizer ameusément l'aureillier; et comme estoit la dicte chaire a portee de son braz, print ce qui luy vint soubz la main.

Or c'estoit cest acoustrement farcy de barbe de baleine, dont les 45r dame[s] honnestes / s'estreignent le corps a celle fin de se tenir droictes et se faire tenures des reins, hormiz que celluy la, on lieu d'estre de toille comme iceulx des aultres damoiselles, estoit faict de beau cuir de roussy, rendent (comme ung chascun scet) odeur trez fort et moult penetratif, ainz bien souef au flair.[44]

Or n'est mestier de vouz dyre quel desduict print Jehan a manier, flairer, et baizer cest acoustreme[n]t, qui debvoit avoir estreint le corps de la belle fille, et par l'usaige en avoit print figure et patron. Neant moing, maulgré le playsir que prenoit a cela, sentit ses paulpieres s'apesantir, et s'endormit.

COMMENT JEHAN FEUT BIEN ESTONNÉ DE S'ESVEIGLER ENS SON LICT /

45v   Estoit ja grant jour quant Jehan s'esvegla, et agardoit partout, cerchant la belle fille. Ainz perdoit son temps, car avoir bien ouvert les oeuilz veid que estoit ens son lict comme de coustume, et on lieu de la belle pucelle ne veid que le Pere Anthoine engenoillé devant le crucifix. Atant, ne sçachant que croyr[e] de tout cela, s'enquesta de luy se estoit bien esveiglé et ne songeoit point en ce moment et qu'estoit deveneue la jeune fille qui avoit sy bien acoustré sa teste a ce que estoit acouchié sus son beau lict.

46r   "Selon ce que tu dis, mon paovre garson," / respondict le pere, "pourroie croyre que tu songes en cest instant, se ne veoie bien apertement que tu ne dors plus et que tout cecy ne peult venir que d'ung songe que tu auras faict. Alons, esveigles toi bien et reprends tes esperitz!"

     "Maulgré et envi ce que distes, bon Pere," reprint Jehan, "me recorde trop bien moy que aprez ma cheute ay reprint cognoissance sus ung lict sy moueleux et sy rich[e] que oncques n'ay esperceu le pareil. Oultre plus, une jeune pucelle belle comme ung ange du paradiz ha acoustré[45] ma playe et m'ha faict boire ens une belle coupe cristalline du vin plus soeuf que nectar, et d'advantaige en ay encore le goust ens la bouche!"

46v   "Ascoutes bien, mon garson," dist le pere, "cecy ne peult / estre que ung songe que tu aras faict! Or va[y] moy te conter comment tout s'est passé: comme tu as deguerpi de chez ton oncle, n'ha esté luy lent a te suy[v]re; et comme tu venois de te lesser cheoir, arrivoit luy sus toy et sanz pitié aulcune t'aroit achevé de tuer, se par fortune n'eust esté la ung homme qui luy ha arrachié le nerf de la main et luy en ha tant baillé que maintenant est este[n]deu sus son lict, dont ne bougera luy de sy tost."

     "Or comment sçavés vouz tout cela?" dist Jehan.

     "Tu doibz te ramenter," respondist le Pere Anthoine, "que La Bechotte s'est eschapee de la maizon ung moment avant toy et est veneue se resfugier chez moy prez de sa tante. Et se ses jambes estoient
47r   lassees, / sa langue ne l'estoit grain, et ha tout conté. Lors, pour te venir en ayde, me suy avoyé par ou cuydoie que tu debvois regaigner ton logiz, et t'ay treuvé estendeu par terre, atout la teste souillee de sang. Lors l'homme qui ha sy bien estrillé ton oncle m'ha aydé a te mectre sus mes espaulles, et t'ay apporté sus ton lict, ou te voyla. Et comme tu n'avois point encore r[e]print cognoissance, ay moy estuvé et acoustré ta playe. Ores reposes toy, et ne penses que a te guarir, aprez quoy ne targera guiaire que ne t'aye treuvé femme qui t'apportera heur et liesse en mesnaige."

"Oh, bon Pere," dist Jehan, "ne me parlés de mariaige depuis mon
47v   songe (puisque volés que ce soyt ung songe); ne veulx aultre / femme que
celle la, ou oncques ne me marieray!"

"Et bien," reprin[t] le pere, "songes seullement a te guarir; en
aprez, veoirons a ce que sera de faire. Ores, come te voyla hors de tout
dangier, te lesse ung peu, et ne targeray."

COMMENT JEHAN FEUT BIEN EMPESCHIÉ ET AMBIGU

Incontinent que le Pere Anthoin[e] se feut parti de la, le povre
Jehan feut bien ambigu de ce que debvoit croyre. D'une part, se
rementoit veu, voire mesme touchié la belle fille, et avoit encore en la
48r   bouche le goust du bon vin que / luy avoit faict bo[i]re elle, et oultre plus,
ses mains avoient encore reteneu l'odeur sy souef de son corsay que avoit
luy tant manié et ameusément ba[i]zé.

D'aultre part, ne pouvoit croyre que le Pere Anthoine, qui en toutes
re[n]contres luy avoit esté tant devost, eust peu le truffer et se jouer de
luy; et tant plus pourpensoit, tant plus cheoit en doubte, pourquoy
pensoit a part soy que le coup que avoit repceu avoit possible peu rendre
fol. En ung mot, ne sçavoit quoy resouldre a sa parfin. Pour en finer,
amprint d'atendre, et pour le moment ne songea plus que a se guarrir;
mais sa guarison se feit peu atendre, pource que le bon pere ne faisoit
faulte a venir le songner toutz les jours.

48v   Or, huict jours / ne s'estoient escoulés que auroit bien peu issir de
l'ost[el], n'eust esté l'ennui de se monsttrer avecques ung fronteau.[46] A la
parfin, tout ala sy bien que sa blessure feut tost reprinse; par ainsy
amprint d'aler l'endemain a la tombe de sa mere, et en aprez chez le bon
Pere Anthoine.

COMMENT JEHAN ALA A LA TOMBE DE SA MERE ET FEUT ESMERVEILLE DES FLEURS QUE Y TREUVA

L'endemain Jehan lessa son lict de bonne heure, car de long temps
49r   n'avoit peu issir de l'ost[el], et avoit besoing de humer ung peu l'aer. / Par

ainsy, se hasta de se vestir et s'avoya tost a la tombe de sa mere tant regrectee.

Or ne peulx vouz dire combien feut luy [estommi]⁴⁷ lors que veid ceste tombe couverte de tant et sy belles fleurs que, n'eust esté la croix, n'aroit on peu veoir que elle estoit la dessoubz. Aussy print luy bonne resolucion de se enquerrir de la personne qui aportoit ces fleurs, affins de l'en bien mercier.

En atendant, s'engenoilla et feit bien devostement sa priere, aprez quoy entra ung moment ens l'ecclize. Or est bien a penser que demanda a Dieu la graace de luy faire rescourre la belle fille, car ne pouvoit encore croyre que c'estoit ung songe; et avoir bien prié, s'avoya chez le bon pere, que treuva tout a poinct et l'embrassa d'affection.

49v   Le bon pere / retint Jehan a dipner, et passarent grant part du jour a devizer entre eulx, aprez quoy le bon pere luy dist:

"Ores que te voyla bien guarri, as du veoir toy a ce que tu as demouré seul sanz issir du logiz que ja est temps de prendre une compaigne, car ne peulx toy vivre tant asseulé."

"Oh, bon Pere," dist Jehan, "ne me parlés de mariaige! Vouz ay ja dict que n'espoulzeray aultre femme que icelle de mon songe: or, comme volés que ce soyt ung songe, oncques ne doib me marier!"

"Soyt," feit le pere, "parlons d'aul[t]r[e]s choses."

"Bon Pere," respondist Jehan, "par avant de venir ceans, ay esté a la tombe de ma mere, et l'ay treuvee encor plus chargiee de fleurs que

50r   avant ma cheute; et suy moy bien / dezireux d'aprendre qui peult les apporter. Vouz qui cognoissés tout, ne pourriez vouz descouvrir cela, affins que puisse moy en tesmoingner ma gratitude?"

"Oh," dist le bon pere, "peulx je te le dyre tout incontinent: ceste personne est une jeune fille belle comme ung ange que ta mere ha defendeue contre aulcuns qui la calomnioient; et par recognoissance apporte elle ces belles fleurs."

"Or, ne pourroie je," dist Jehan, "aler l'en mercier?"

"Non seullement tu le peulx, mais tu le doibs," reprint le bon pere. "Viens demain a la vespree souper avecques moy, et en aprez te meineray chez elle."

Tout estant ainsy conveneu, n'en feut plus mencion, et toutz deux 50v passarent la reste du / jour a deviser entre eulx.

COMMENT PAR LES BONS OFFICES DU BON PERE JEHAN ATEINGNIT AU COMBLE DE SES SOUHAICTZ

Comme estoit conveneu, le jour esuyvant a la vespree Jehan ala chez le Pere Anthoine, qui l'attendoit et luy dist:

"Hersoir t'avoie[48] dict que irons chez la damoiselle aprez[49] souper. Ores cuyde je que fairons bien mieulx d'y aller avant; par ainsy souperons plus tranquilement, et pourrons deviser tout a nostre bandon. Atant n'avons que a nous avoier."

51r   Le bon pere prouficta que estoit annui / pour meiner Jehan par chemins destournés tant que arrivarent a une ruelle jouxte une mazure du tout ruynee, et entrare[n]t dedanz, et n'eusrent faict dix paz que le bon pere tira de sa pouche une clef et ouvrit une faulse porte donnant sus ung beau courtil, et entrarent. Et avoir songneusement reclos l'huis, le Pere Anthoine dist a Jehan que se par adventure la jeune fille estoit a son apetit, povoit luy demander sa main sanz craincte de refuz.

Atant le bon pere ouvrit ung[50] aultre huis et le poulsa dedanz une chambre, luy disant: "Demoures la, a ce que vay anun[c]er ta veneue."

Or pensés quel feust l'estonnement de Jehan lors que veid luy a 51v n'en doubter que ceste chambre estoit icelle de son songe! / Rien n'y faisoit desfaulte que la belle fille, et disoit a part soy:

"Le Pere Anthoine m'auroit il ensorcelé, ou cecy n'est il encore qu'ung songe, ou suy je fol? Toute foy, vecy bien le lict ou estoie lors que ha elle acoustré ma teste. Voila bien les beaulx meubles et tout."

Pourquoy ne sçavoit que croyre quant entendist quelque[s] paz, dont feut esmeu jusques au tresfund de sa fressure, cuydant que ce povoit estre la belle fille qui venoit—et ne faisoit erreur, car une porte s'ouvrit et entra elle, faisant une belle et gratieuse reverance. Atant le bon Jehan ne peut laschier ung [mot], tant estoit pantois et aheu[r] i.

     Or notés que Jehan n'avoit encore veu ceste fille divine que
52r   simplement vestue d'une robbe / de nuict et sanz aulcuns ornements, mais en ce moment elle estoit tant bien acesmee, atisee, affieree, et aorne[e] que estoit esblouissante a veoir.

     Ses beaulx chevueilz noirs gentement[51] attifés etoient enlassés d'ung fil d'unions indicques; de ses petites mignonnes aureilles pendoient deux esmeraugdes de haulte valeue, et avoit a son col ung riche collier de adamantz, estincelent de lumiere; son genty gorgiaz descouvroit legierement ses blanches espaulles, sy point assiez que on ne peut dezirer en veoir d'advantaige! Et avoit une robbe de damas bleu, dont le corsaige estreingnoit sy voluptueusement et ameusément son corps que
52v   en resveloit naïfvement formes et contours. Et la / jupe, richement brodee d'or a l'esguille entortillee, descendoit jus mais point sy bas que on ne peut veoir ses piedz d'anfant gentement chaussés de jolis petitz mignons brodequins de soye bien lassés et orlés par en hault d'une frenge d'or. Et avoit a ses mains de beaulx guantz de peau trez deliee reteneus au bas du braz par des armilles d'or acoust[r]ees de coural. Ainz est bien temps que r[e]venons a Jehan.

     La belle fille, le veant tant estommi, luy dist: "Et bien, Messire, ne recognoissés vouz celle qui ha eu l'heur de vouz assist[er] en vostre meschoie?" Et le prenant par la main le meina a ung bel aclinouer et s'assit a costé de luy.

     "Oh, belle damoiselle!" dist Jehan, "escusés ma lourdize! Le Pere
53r   Anthoine ha tant destourbé / mes esperitz que ne pourroye je affermer se tout cecy est songe ou verité, pourquoy au nom de Dieu vouz conjure de me dyre se suy moy bien esveiglé."

     "Messire," respondist elle, "tout cecy n'est point plus ung songe que c'en estoit ung lors que vouz ay faict mectre sus mon lict que voyla; et ay pansé vostre blessure autant bien que ay peu. Seullement, avoie mis danz le vin que vouz ay baillé a boire ung peu d'ung liqueur soporifiant, et incontinent que le sommeil vouz ha print, le bon Pere Anthoine (que avoie faict venir) et mon serf vouz ont emporté ens vostre lict. Et se le bon pere ha vouleu vouz faire croyre que aviés resvé cela, ne luy en
53v   gardés rancueur, car avoit luy bonnes raisons pour / faire ainsy."

"Lors, comme est ainsy," dist Jehan, "doib vouz dyre que suy veneu ceans pour vouz tesmoingner ma gratitude, tant pour le bon souvenir que gardés de ma mere que pour les belles fleurs que apportés sus sa tombe. D'advantaige, auroye bien une graace a vouz demander; ainz n'auze le dire, tant suy indigne de l'obtenir."

"Dites toutz jours," dist l'adorable fille.

"Or, par ainsy que le permettés," dist Jehan, "ce seroyt d'obtenir vostre main. Or mon sort depend de vouz, car d'ung mot pouvés faire de moy le plus beat ou le plus malheureux des hommes!"

"Messire," respondist elle, "ay moy trop grant estime de vouz que 54r face moy vostre malheur; sy doib vouz dyre que en cecy n'agissés / point ne saigement ne preudentement, car dema[n]dés vouz ma main sanz sçavoir quelle je suy ne dond je vien ne quelz sont mes parentz. Oultre plus, ne pourriez vouz dyre mon nom."

"Oh," feit Jehan, "ne me chault de tout cela, et n'ay cure que de devenir vost[r]e espoulx!"

"Voire mais," feit elle, "et se par adventure estoye la Juifve?"

"Oh," dist Jehan, "n'ay craincte de cela!"

Atant l'adorable fille se leva, majestueuse comme une royne et, tendent le braz vers Jehan, luy dist: "Se tant est que le dezir de m'espoulzer vouz poinct, debvés sçavoir quelle je suy. Or escoutés! Je suy naye es montz caucazians et nomme[e] Noemi, et suy fille du juif Ozias, mort encea quellesque[s] anne[e]s et ensepulturé ens mon 54v courtil. En ung mot, avés devant / vouz ceste afre Juifve sorciere, puant le soulfre, mauldicte, et resfuie de tout le munde. Ores voulés vouz de moy?"

Jehan ne peut respondre, tant estoit estommi; mais se jecta a ses piedz et les baiza avecques ardeur. Tout incontinent la belle Noemi le feit lever, et luy dist:

"Tenés, prenés ma main, et que tout soyt dict. Le bon Pere Anthoine vouz m[e]ctera tout en appert; et est temps que[52] allons le rejoindre, car nous attend luy pour souper."

Avoir dict, la belle Juifve print Jehan par la main et le meina ens la chambre voyzine, ou treuvarent le bon pere assiz devant une table sumptueusement acoustree de vaisselle de haulte valeue et couverte des
55r viandes / les plus friandes et des vins les plus exquis. Tout incontinent que entrarent eulx, alarent accoler le bon pere qui plouroit d'ayse. Finablement s'assirent a table; souparent gentement et berent de hait, car le vin estoit alichant. Et comme estoient en propoz de devizer entre eulx, le Pere Anthoine dist a Jehan:

"Ores te voyla bien content; neant moing, n'as tu pensé a tout, car Noemi est juifve et toy christian, et ne void je comment cela pourra s'arrengier."

"Oh," feit Jehan, "n'ay cure de cela, car ne m'ariés vouz amené ceans se eust esté empeschement aulcun a la chose."

"En cela tu as bien jugé de moy," dist le bon pere, "et t'en rend
55v graaces! Aprends doncques que le jour de ton mariaige, ta belle / Noemi repcévra le baptesme, et oultre plus aura elle pour parrein nostre venerable evesque. Et aprends aussy que se t'ay enhorté a croyre que ta Noemi n'estoit que ung songe, c'est que oncque n'auroie voleu te la veoir espoulzer juifve, et n'est que l'aultre hier que ha elle assenti a repcevoir le baptesme. Et la coerimonie aura lieu danz quatre jours. Par ainsy, apreste toy!"

EXPLICIT l'istoyre de Jehan Coquault et de la belle Juifve. S'elle ha peu, Chier Lecteur, vouz recreer tant seullement ung petit, n'auray perdeu ma poyne. Et ne targeray a vouz conter icelle du grant Baya, comme vouz l'ay proumiz. En atendent, prie a Dieu qu'il vouz doinst paix et liesse ens ce munde et son Paradiz en l'aultre.

NOTES AND REJECTED READINGS

[1] The title given here *(Antiennes cronicques...)* differs from the one that follows the prologue. There (fol. 3r), in a section title, we read "S'ensuit l'Istoyre de Jehan Coquault." Perhaps we should see *Istoyre* as a title and *Cronicques* as a description or a generic designation. A third—and unreliable—title is given on the spine of the volume: *Anciennes Cronicques de Reims* (a title followed by "Jean Coquault," which was apparently taken as an indication of authorship). The *explicit* reads "Explicit l'istoyre de Jehan Coquault et de la belle Juifve."

[2] The story of the *Grant Baya de Rains* was presumably to follow that of Jehan Coquault. The conclusion of the *Cronicques* refers once again to it. It is not preserved in the Spencer manuscript, however, and I have found no reference to it elsewhere.

[3] MS: *attendeu.*

[4] This section heading is apparently misplaced, since the author continues for one more paragraph the account of his discovery of the manuscript. Logically, the section begins after the sentence "Ores je commence . . . amen," at the bottom of fol. 3r.

[5] MS: *icellez.* During the Middle French period, a final z (following e) came to have specific diacritical value, indicating that the preceding vowel was close; i.e., [e]. In the *Coquault* manuscript, that is always its function in final -ez, with the exception of *icellez* and the *ellez* that follows a few words later; I emend those two forms to *icelles* and *elles.*

[6] MS: *ellez.* See n. 5.

[7] MS: *une une.*

[8] *Que* is an acceptable form. In general, this use of *que* as subject (where we would expect Modern French *qui*) is limited to feminine or neuter *que,* but it does occasionally occur in the masculine. See Brunot, II, 317. A similar form occurs on 16v: *ce que estoit necessaire.*

[9] MS: *que ne cuyde moy que.*

[10] MS: *voste. Voste* occurs also on 43r, 54r. R frequently drops in sixteenth-century texts both after an unvoiced plosive and before final e. *Voste, vot'* may thus be acceptable forms, although the r is generally written even when silent. In the three cases noted here, however, I emend to *vost[r]e,* on the basis of some dozen occurrences of *vostre* (6r, 33r, 35r and elsewhere).

[11] *Avoir entendeu:* this construction, the equivalent of *ayant entendu* or *après avoir entendu,* is frequent in Rabeláis and elsewhere; it occurs repeatedly in the *Coquault.*

[12]MS: *les les.*

[13]The sentence appears to be lacking a verb—unless the contorted sentence is intended to depict the anguished and disjointed utterances of Jehan's mother. In any case, we have no basis for emendation.

[14]The identification of the Jewess as a sorceress is not surprising, whatever the date of the *Coquault.* Such accusations were traditional, dating from as far back as the twelfth century. See John F. Benton, ed., *Self and Society in Medieval France: The Memoirs of Abbot Guibert of Nogent* (New York: Harper & Row, 1970), p. 10. See also Venetia Newall's essay "The Jew as a Witch Figure," in *The Witch Figure,* ed. Venetia Newall (London, 1973), pp. 95-124. A few lines later, the Jewess is described as having green eyes like those of a black cat—a small detail that may nonetheless recall the traditional association of witches with black cats (the animals whose shape was frequently assumed by sorceresses).

[15]In the MS, the *en* that ends 11r is repeated at the top of 11v.

[16]*Cimetiere* was generally feminine during the sixteenth century (in Scève, for example). Cotgrave and others, however, list it as a masculine noun, and I leave it. The only other questionable gender I have noted in the MS is *une huis* (51r), which is doubtless a simple error.

[17]MS: *ale.* Presumably, an imperfect is required by the *cependent que.* Although the form may well be *alè* (a scribal representation of an imperfect *aloit,* with the loss of the *w* sound from the ending), emendation seems in order, as this is the only such occurrence in the manuscript.

[18]Of course, she did nothing of the sort. Oudart spoke to her about marriage and about Jehan's inheritance; in response, she mentioned only that Jehan could take care of business matters himself and that, if he did need help, he could call on Anthoine.

[19]MS: *fillotte.*

[20]Although there is no consistent use of name symbolism in the work, "Le Brenou" cannot help but call to mind the word *brenoux* used by Rabelais and others; Cotgrave writes it *breneux* and defines it as "beshitten."

[21]*Ost* generally means either "army" or an "encampment." It can refer specifically to an assemblage of tents or shelters, but the reference is still military. I emend here and elsewhere.

[22]MS: *fillotte.*

[23]The manuscript is evidently defective at this point; the emendation proposed is the simplest of the possibilities.

[24]Concerning *retire* (and *cerche* from 41r), see my remarks above, p. 19.

[25]*Ayguerie* is the only word I have noted in the text that does not appear to be attested during the sixteenth century. It is, however, attested in the nineteenth century, where it is synonymous with *aiguage,* the right to bring water through another's property by use of an aqueduct. In one isolated instance, *aiguerie* refers instead to a reservoir or the aqueduct itself (see *Trésor de la langue française,* ed. Paul Imbs [Paris: C.N.R.S., 1971—], I, 290. While the right to transport water across property does not fit the context, the notion of a reservoir (though not a pipeline) could be justified. It would be tempting, in this single case, to conclude that a nineteenth-century word crept into the text (a small slip by the forger, as it were). But it may also be that *ayguerie* is a perfectly proper sixteenth-century word that simply has not found its way into standard dictionaries. The root *(aigue)* clearly existed, as did *aiguière* (a vase or pitcher). It is notable that this word occurs in one of the few corrupt or problematical passages of the work. This clause and the next one appear to repeat the same general idea; moreover, either a preposition or a verb is evidently omitted before *ma cruche,* while *sus,* although possible, is used uncharacteristically here.

[26]MS: *Ppasquette.*

[27]MS: *tempe.*

[28]*Barri:* I do not find *barri* elsewhere, and the meaning is not clear. Of course, a final *l* after *i* was frequently silent in sixteenth-century French; the pronunciation of *baril* was thus [bari]. Perhaps we should see this word as *barril,* although final *l* is always written elsewhere in the manuscript. We would then have a reference to a rain-barrel or a reservoir of some kind.

[29]The scribe uses *alanuitan* a number of times, and it is always written clearly as one word. It is not elsewhere attested in that form, so far as I can determine. *Anuiter* (or *anuyter*) is frequent, and apparently *alanuitan* is *a l'anuitan*[*t*], the "coming of night," at night(fall). Although the scribe is consistent in the spelling and usage of the word, I emend for clarity, without however adding [*t*].

[30]The sentence lacks a subject. We might conclude that Anthoine decided in the midst of his utterance that Le Brenou would receive more comfort from alcohol generously applied than from his personal assurances; he might therefore have interrupted himself to offer another drink and save his own time and effort. But, while that assessment of Le Brenou is correct, it would be out of character for the decisive Anthoine to begin any sentence that will not require finishing. My emendation, although admittedly pure hypothesis, is supported by the sense of the passage.

[31]Cotgrave, among others, defines *anui* as "today." Clearly, the meaning here (as well as on 50v) is "at night." On 23v, however, the usage of the word agrees with Cotgrave's definition.

[32]"Poetic justice" is expressed with a pleasing symmetry here. When Le Brenou learned of La Sagotte's infanticide, she blackmailed him to keep him quiet (using a kind of "Potiphar's wife" technique: if he reveals the killing, she will say he participated in it). Once he does eventually reveal it to Anthoine, the priest uses the information to blackmail La Sagotte to further his own and Jehan's ends.

[33]MS writes *parchemins* but bars the *p*, giving *pararchemins*.

[34]MS: *avvoir.*

[35]An *asguillette* is a "point" or a string with a tag, used for tying together parts of a dress.

[36]*Corps:* a *corps* can be either a woman's undergarment or specifically the part of a garment covering the upper portion of the body. *Busqué* means provided with *buscs,* which are metal or whalebone stays or ribs. *Corps busqué* thus indicates a ribbed corset or undergarment.

[37]By this time, Oudart has given up the idea of a marriage between Jehan and Remiette, but he has not despaired of acquiring the young man's money. His methods have simply changed from marriage to sorcery and seduction—but still using his daughter as bait.

[38]As I have noted above (p. 19), *va* is a possible form when the subject is *moy,* although it is used primarily in cases where the subject is followed by the relative pronoun: *moy qui va.* See Gougenheim, p. 223. I emend *va moy* to *va[y] moy* here and on 46v. I also emend to *va[y]* on 41r, where the subject is not expressed.

[39]Clearly, there is a lacuna here. La Sagotte has mentioned four letters, while only three are actually noted. The *atant* suggests that it is the first one that is omitted; presumably, the upper right corner should contain "O" (Oudart).

[40]MS: *le le.*

[41]MS: *talonn* (*talõn* with nasal bar).

[42]MS: *estoit.* This is an unusual but attested third-person plural. See Brunot (II, 332), who mentions *ils avoet* and notes that this orthography simply indicates that *-oient* is a single syllable, with the *n* silent and with the vowels *oe* pronounced *wɛ.* However, since the manuscript offers no other example of such a plural, it may well be an error, and I emend.

[43]The contrast between this scene and the preceding one is striking. Remiette had tried to give Jehan a *poison,* but forewarned, he had refused to drink it. Now another woman offers him a beverage, and he is understandably reluctant to take it. Once he is reassured, he drinks it with pleasure—only to learn later that it too was drugged. Thus, one of the scenes reflects the other, and the thematic similarity emphasizes the contrasting motives of the two women, one acting to subjugate him, the other to cure and restore him.

[44]Here, evidently, is the source of the odor emitted by the Jewess. It will be recalled that Jehan's mother admitted that the Jewess gave off an odor, although she questioned whether it was sulphur or some other odor. At that time, she appeared to share certain of the local prejudices about the Jewess (even though she defended her); now, however, her statement is found to be literally correct.

[45]MS: *acoustee.*

[46]A *fronteau* is a band or cloth worn around the head—in this case, a bandage. But a *fronteau* was in particular a headband worn by Jews, a fact that may not be without significance. Jehan's hesitation to show himself in public wearing a *fronteau* may evoke once again the apparently anti-semitic climate of the work, even though he himself is still unaware that his benefactress is the Jewess.

[47]The meaning is clear from the context, but *estommi* is a hypothesis; *esmerveillé* (from the section title) would be equally appropriate.

[48]MS: *avoiie.*

[49]MS: *avant que;* emended for sense (see preceding section, as well as the following sentence).

[50]MS: *une.*

[51]MS: *gentemennt* (written *gentemènt*).

[52]MS: *qallons* (apparently for $\bar{q}$ *allons*).

INDEX OF PROPER NAMES

Anthoine (Père Anthoine); the Coquault family priest, Jehan's protector.

Baya (Le Grant Baya de Rains): the character and title of another work, promised but not included in the manuscript.

Bechote, La: another name for Pasquette.

Brenou, Le: La Sagotte's servant; real name Pierre.

Coquault, André: Jehan's father.

Coquault, Jehan: the principal character of the work.

Coquault, Magdeleine: Jehan's aunt; (deceased) wife of Oudart.

Gaultier, Claude: father of one of Remiette's consorts.

Gobreau, Magdelon: another name for La Sagotte.

Noemi: the Jewess, future wife of Jehan.

Oudart: Jehan's uncle and adversary; see also Remiette.

Ozias: father of Noemi.

Pasquette: niece of Ursule and chambermaid of Remiette; also called La Bechote.

Pierre: another name for Le Brenou.

Remiette (Remiette Oudart): Jehan's cousin, ally of her father Oudart in attempts to defraud Jehan.

Sagotte, La: sorceress; real name Magdelon Gobreau.

Ursule: Anthoine's servant; Pasquette's aunt.

GLOSSARY

This glossary lists items required to permit a reader of Modern French to understand the text. It thus includes words that no longer exist, words that have become rare or that have changed in meaning since the sixteenth century, and forms that are not readily recognizable. Since spellings of certain words vary from page to page, I list the most frequent form or, in some cases, the form in which it first occurs. Verbs are listed under the infinitive, and the conjugated form is given only when it differs sufficiently from the infinitive to prevent immediate recognition. A certain number of past participles are listed and identified as adjectives, if that is their only use in the text.

In the preparation of this glossary I have made most extensive use of Edmond Huguet's *Dictionnaire de la langue française du seizième siècle* and have also consulted early sources, primarily the dictionnaries of Cotgrave and Palsgrave.

A *prep* with

ABAUBI *adj* astonished

ACCOISER *v* calm

ACCORT *adj* capable

ACCOUSTRER *v* decorate, provide

ACCRAVANTER *v* burst out, appear

ACERTAINER *v* ascertain

ACESMÉ *adj* adorned

ACCESSEMENT *nm* adornment, accoutrement

ACLINOUER *nm* couch

ACOURT *prep* during; ACOURT QUE *conj* while

ACOUSTRER *v* prepare, provide with; look after

ADAMANT *nm* diamond

ADMONESTER *v* admonish

ADVERTISSEMENT *nm* warning

AFFECTER *v* have affection for, desire

AFFIER *v* affirm, certify

AFFIERÉ *adj* adorned

AFRE *adj* frightful, horrible

AGARDER *v* look

AGREANTER *v* please

AHEURI *adj* astonished, dismayed

AINS *conj* rather

AIQUES *indef pron* something

ALICHER *v* attract; ALICHANT *adj* delicious, appealing

AMARY *nm* vagina

AMBIGU *adj* confused

AMEUSÉMENT *adv* thoroughly, carefully

AMPRENDRE *v* undertake

ANGELOT *nm* small coin

ANUI *adv* today, at night

AORNER (S') *v* adorn oneself

APAROIR *v* appear

APERT *adj* evident

AQUOISER *v* calm

ARMILLE *nf* bracelet

ARSOIR: *see* HERSOIR

ARTIFICIEUSEMENT *adv* artfully

ASCOUTER *v* listen; EN ASCOUT: attentive, listening

ASGUILLETTE *nf* lace, cord, point

ASSAIER *v* try

ASSEMBLER *v* resemble

ASSERER *v* assert

ASSEULÉ *adj* alone

ASTOU *adv, prep* around

ATANT *adv* then

ATOURER (S') *v* comb, adorn

ATOUT *prep* with, along with

ATTIFÉ *adj* adorned

ATTISÉ *adj* animated

ATTREMPÉ *adj* disciplined

AVOYER (S') *v* set out

AYGUERIE *nf* well (?)

BAHUT *nm* large chest

BAILLER *v* give

BAIZER *v, nm* kiss

BANDON *nm* freedom, license

BARRI *nm* barrel (?)

BAULDEMENT *adv* freely, merrily

BEAT *adj* happy

BEAUGEAR *nm* scoundrel

BENDER (SE) *v* make effort, set about

BERENT: *3 pl. pret. of* BEIRE, BOIRE (drink)

BEVETER *v* drink

BIGARÉ *adj* of mingled colors

BOUQUON *nm* poison

BOURDE *nf* joke

BOURE *nf* down, material used for tents, mattresses, etc.

BREUSSE *nf* drinking vessel

BRODEQUIN *nm* light shoe, buskin

BUSQUÉ *adj* ribbed

CAGOUT *nm* hypocrite

CAQUETER *v* gossip, babble

CAULT *adj* crafty

CEAN *adv* in, in here

CHEVANCE *nf* possessions, inheritance

CHIFFREMENT *nm* plotting, scheming

CHOPPER *v* strike

CINGERIE *nf* trickery

COMPLAINDRE *v* complain

COMPLAYRE *v* please

CONVENANT *adj* proper, appropriate

CORPS *nm* woman's undergarment

CORSAY *nm* corset

COTTE *nf* dress, coat

COULON *nm* dove, pigeon

COURAL *nm* coral

COURTIL *nm* courtyard, small garden

COUTIL *nm* quilt, mattress

CUYDIER *v* think

DEFFENDRE (SE) *v* help, prevent oneself

DEGUERPIR *v* leave

DEHAIT *adv* willingly

DEMENER (SE) *v* toss and turn

DESCHAUX *adj* barefoot

DESPESTRER (SE) *v* disengage oneself

DEVISER *v* discuss, plan

DOST *nf* dowry

DRESSOUER *nm* dresser, bureau

DREZ *prep* since, after

DUICT *adj* experienced

EMBLER *v* steal

EMPLIR *v* fill

ENCEA *prep* since; *adj* ago (also ENÇA)

ENCQUETER *v* chat, ask questions

ENCUSER *v* betray, inform against

ENDAZ *interj* in truth, on my word

ENDEMAIN *nm* following day

ENDEMENÉ *adj* lascivious, wanton

ENDURANT *adj* patient

ENGINER *v* deceive

ENHORTER *v* exhort

ENHUY *adv* today

ENQUESTER (S') *v* inquire

ENTORTILLÉ *adj* wrapped, twisted

ENTRAVER *v* block, defeat

ENVI *prep;* MALGRÉ ET ENVI: in spite of

ENVISAIGER *v* see (someone) face to face

ENVOUSTER *v* subjugate, charm

ESBATTEMENT *nm* pleasure

ESCUELLE *nf* dish

ESGUILLONNÉ *adj* tormented

ESLONGNEMENT *nm* reluctance

ESPERCEVOIR *v* see

ESPREINDRE *v* squeeze out

ESSE = EST-CE

ESSEUIL *nm* threshold

ESTOMMI *adj* astonished

ESTOUPÉ *adj* stopped, corked

ESTREIN *nm* straw

ESTRIF *nm* grief, upset

ESTUVER *v* bathe

ESVEIGLER (S') *v* awaken

EXISTIMER *v* consider

FASSON *nm* way

FIANCE *nf* confidence

FLAIRER *v* smell

FLEURS *nf pl* menstrual period (fol. 30v, 32r only)

FRANGEE *nf* mark, stripe

FRONTEAU *nm* band worn around the head

FOUACE *nf* cake

FRESSURE *nf* being

GAUSSER (SE) *v* mock

GENT *adj* attractive

GLUE *nf* birdlime

GORGIAZ *nm* wimple, gorget

GOUZIER *nm* throat, mouth

GRABELER *v* examine carefully

GRAIN: NE . . . GRAIN *adv* not

GEUDOUFLE *nf* bottle with rounded bottom

GUERDONNÉ *adj* rewarded

GUEUZER *v* beg

HA: *3 sg. ps. of* AVOIR (= il y a): ago

HAIM *nm* fishook

HAIT: *see* DEHAIT

HANTER (SE) *v* frequent

HERSOIR *adv* yesterday evening

HOIRIE *nf* inheritance

HOUPE *nf* decoration, assemblage of threads

HUMER *v* taste, drink, smell

HUMETTER *v* taste, drink

HUY *adv* today

HYPOCRAS *nm* mulled wine

ICELLUY *dem adj* that

INCONTINENT *adv* immediately; INCONTINENT QUE: as soon as

INDICQUE *adj* Indian

JAÇOIT QUE *conj* although

JACTER (SE) *v* boast

JARD *nm* garden

JAYET *nm* jet

JAZER *v* talk, babble

JONCHÉ *adj* strewn

JOUXTE *prep* beside

JUS *adv* down

LAQ *nm* net, trap

LANGUER *v* tell

LECTION *nf* reading

MAL *adj* evil, grave; MALE SEPMAINE: menstrual period

MATOIZ *nm* deceitful, crafty

MAZURE *nf* ruins of a house

MENEE *nf* subterfuge

MESCHOIR *nm* misfortune

MESHAIGNE *adj* distressed

MESHUY *adv* today, from now on

MESTIER *nm;* ESTRE MESTIER it is necessary

MIGNARDIZE *nf* wantonness, seductive speech

MIGNOTTE *adj* wanton, playful

MILLIAIRE *nm* date

MISTION *nf* misture, potion

MITAN *nm* middle

MORISQUE *nm, adj* Moor, Moorish

MOUELEUX *adj* sumptuous, luxurious

MUSSER *v* hide

NAÏFVEMENT *adv* directly, openly

NAY: *p. part. of* NAISTRE (born)

NENNY *adv* no

NERF DE BOEUF *nm* whip

NOISE *nf* conflict, noise

NOIZILLE *nf* hazel nut

NONOBSTANT *prep* notwithstanding; —QUE *conj* notwithstanding the fact that

OBSTER *v* object

OIZEL *nm* bird

ON: *contract. of* EN LE (in)

ONCQUES *adv* never

ORD *adj* dirty

ORES *adv* now

ORLÉ *adj* bordered

OSTEL *nm* domicile

OYANT *pres. part of* OÏR (hear)

PANTOIS *adj* breathless, astonished

PARTANT *adv* therefore

PAS *nm* passage

PIEÇA *adv* (long) ago

PIGEONNERIE *nf* lascivious kiss

PINART *nm* small coin

PLOYER *v* bend

POELE *nm* canopy of bed

POURCHAZ *nm* matter, pursuit

POURMENER (SE) *v* walk

PREIGNE *adj* pregnant

PREUDE *adj* good, noble

PRISER *v* consider

PROU *adj and n* many, much

PROUVOYANCE *nf* foresight, caution; PROUVEOYANT *adj* prudent, cautiou

PUTZ *nm* well

QUARÉ *nm* square

QUARROY *nm* highway

RAMENTER (SE) *v* remember

RECHIGNER *v* frown, act in a surly manner

RECREER *v* entertain

RESCOURRE *v* recover, find

RESFUI *adj* shunned, avoided

ROLLE *nm* manuscript, scroll

ROUSSY *nm* reddish-brown leather

RUER *v* rush

SAPIENCE *nf* wisdom

SCHEDULE *nf* signed document

SEMONCE *nf* warning

SEMONDRE *v* summon, beseech, invite

SEQUELLE *nf* companions, company

SINGLADE *nf* blow

SOLACION *nf* consolation

SOUEF *adj* sweet

SOUILLÉ *adj* soiled

SOULDART *nm* soldier

SOULOIR *v* to be accustomed to

TARGER *v* delay; TARGEMENT *nm* delay

TAUDI *nm* shelter; poor dwelling

TENELLEMENT *adv* delicately

TESTONNER (SE) *v* curl hair; comb hair

TIROUER *nm* drawer

TORTEAU *nm* cake, round form

TRAC *nm:* A TRAC deliberately

TRAINEE *nf* temptation

TRANSON *nm* piece, bit

TRESFUND *nm* depth

TRESPASSER *v* die

TRESQUE *prep* until

TRUFER *v* mock, deceive

VEGUADE *nf* glassful, drink

VEIGLEE *nf* wake

VEOIRÉS: *2 pl. fut. of* VEOIR (see)

VIAIRE *nm* face, countenance

VISER *v* intend; VISEE *nf* intention

VOULTE *nf:* FAIRE BONNE VOULTE charm, attract

ZIVETTE *nf* civet